calgary avansino

keep it real

calgary avansino

keep it real

CREATE A HEALTHY, BALANCED AND DELICIOUS LIFE — FOR YOU AND YOUR FAMILY

To my three glorious children – Ava, Margot and Remy
– you split my every heartbeat in thirds.

contents

Introduction: my 'real' story   8

01   Plant-powered living: *why plants will make you feel amazing*   14

02   Getting organised: *simple steps for healthy living*   34

03   Pantry staples: *how to fill your cupboards with goodness*   60

04   Sugar: *where it hides and how to ditch it*   98

05   Breakfast: *wake up and smell the real food*   122

06   Family: *eating nutritiously together*   134

07   Recipes   154

Index   250

Acknowledgements   255

I was raised on the west coast of America (Nevada and California) by parents who taught me from a young age the importance of cooking meals from scratch, the power of eating real food and the role nutrition plays in looking and feeling your best. I was lucky to be immersed in that environment during my most impressionable years, and what I learned then – mostly just by watching and experiencing – has stuck with me throughout my life. Of course I went through a rebellious teenage period when I ate rubbish (and felt rubbish), but everything I had learned re-emerged when I came to my senses, and from then on my interest and passion in health and well-being has only grown.

Sixteen years ago I moved to London and started a family five years later. I continue to try my hardest to pass down these important lessons by example – through my everyday choices and actions – to my own family, as well as to friends and colleagues. And now I want to share them all with you too.

I'm not a nutritionist or a trained chef; however, the things I most definitely hold degrees in are being a working mum to three children, a wife and a friend and colleague who loves cooking, eating and feeding others healthy food. I started writing about nutritious food and well-being for *Vogue* and the *Sunday Times* 'Style' magazines simply because people kept asking me for guidance. They wanted to know what I ate, how I stocked my kitchen, how I cooked and how I fed my children. It was this curiosity and my friends' and colleagues' desire to be healthier that motivated me to start this career, and it is still what drives me every day. Now, when I write an article or post a recipe that results in readers' letters telling me about the transformations they've made to their lives, it is an incredible feeling. To see positive change emerge is the most rewarding result.

My credentials are very simply years in the kitchen working with ingredients and keeping them real, trying new combinations and creating nutritious meals that my family and friends think are delicious. So if you are looking for gourmet recipes or fancy food that takes hours to prep, this is not the book for you. While I love concocting new recipes, at heart I am all about simple, quick and easy cooking that is just as full of goodness as it is flavour. Who doesn't want a bit of that combination in their life?

swapping negative for positive

This book is not about dieting or losing weight or counting calories. I will not be telling you to skip meals or deny yourself – just the opposite. This book is about being kind to yourself, replacing all those bad habits with good ones and filling yourself up with the best possible food available to give you a sense of well-being and achievement. So all I want you to do is commit to yourself that you will try. That is the first step – hear yourself say 'I want to try'. Even if you don't make any practical changes for a few weeks, I want

you to start thinking about yourself as someone who is worth trying for. You are just as much worthy of your love as others who receive your love and attention. This is often the first obstacle when things feel overwhelming, but it's amazing what a powerful agent the mind can be when it is on your side, cheering you on, saying, 'Yes, I want to try' and 'Yes, I am worth trying for'. It is never too late to start, nor is any situation too far gone. Every day, every meal and every bite is an opportunity to make changes and to start caring enough about how you feel, look and function. Every person deserves to feel energetic, be full of enthusiasm for life and to look as good as they feel. No one should think that is unattainable. It is attainable and I want to help you reach that goal.

Why do I believe this so strongly? Because I have seen it work time and time again. Change happens when you decide you are going to try. I've witnessed this with countless friends and colleagues who have committed to changing the way they think, shop for and prepare their food. Some have taken the all-or-nothing approach, making big and broad lifestyle changes all at once, while others have progressed slowly, committing to small changes and slowly transforming to a plant-based, real-food lifestyle. Guess what? Either way they have all experienced a remarkable revolution in how they feel: enjoying more energy, fewer mood swings, fewer cravings, losing weight and generally feeling really great about themselves for making the effort and creating change in themselves.

You can experience all these benefits too. We all have voices in our heads, which can sometimes be pretty negative, but this journey towards health is as much a mental process as a physical one, and it starts by turning down the volume of your negative voice and turning up the positive one. What you say to yourself makes such a huge difference, so start being nicer to the only you that you've got. Remind yourself on a daily basis that you've made a commitment to changing the way you eat, changing the way you feel and changing the way you look – for you.

your 'real food' journey

I believe more than anything else in the importance of eating real food. And let me be clear about exactly what that means: food that is grown in the soil, on trees and on bushes with the sun's energy. Boxes of cookies, bars wrapped in plastic and packages of refined foods are not real. They are manufactured in factories and contain an endless array of processed ingredients.

To transform your health and your life together we need to go back to the basics of food. Change will not happen for you until you prioritise real and wholesome foods that are created by Mother Nature, rather than by an assembly line. This is what plant-based living is all about. Throughout this book I am going to explain exactly what it means to prioritise plants, show you how to cook with more plants and reveal just how much better you can feel if you make the shift to a plant-based lifestyle. To some this may sound like a simple, achievable concept and to others it may feel daunting. Either way I am with you on every page, to support your journey towards health and a positive relationship with food. Step by step we will learn why filling every plate with more plants is important, how to cut down the sugar in your diet, how to replace wheat and gluten with delicious alternatives, how to make simple healthy swaps and how to cook easy recipes using real ingredients. If someone asked me to summarise how to completely transform your health and body in the simplest way possible, these would be my five golden rules:

01   Give up on diets *forever* . . . forever. Plant-based living is a fulfilling, satisfying, permanent lifestyle, not a punishing, painful period of deprivation.

02   Eat real food – food grown from the earth.

03   Eat less refined, processed, ready-made food.

04   Learn the truth about sugar – and where it hides – and start eliminating it from your diet.

05   Make an effort to move your body every day.

Really, it's that simple. Over the next few chapters I'm going to help you make these rules your way of life too. Remember, you don't need to make all of these changes at once. You can just take it one step at a time. Don't expect everything to change immediately but know that change will happen if you commit to trying.

how we're going to do this together

We're all busy these days so I have consciously written this book to make it as easy as possible to kick-start a healthy lifestyle and maintain one. Each chapter is packed with simple guidelines you can incorporate into your life one at a time. There are lots of bite-sized ideas for you to try and step-by-step plans that are realistic and achievable. I will guide you through shopping for a plant-based lifestyle and stocking your cupboards in the most nutritious way. I will also show you how simple it can be to reduce sugar, gluten and wheat in your diet, and I'll excite and inspire you with simple plant-based recipes that I have tried and tested at home.

When it comes to our children and what they eat, I have a lot to say. I want every parent to feel that change is possible – it's never too late to incorporate healthy ideas into family meals, snacks and school lunches. To give you as much information as possible, I have included child-friendly tips throughout the book and have dedicated a chapter to working plant-based living into family life, how to reduce sugar from your children's diets and how to encourage them to try new foods.

the new you

Don't think that just because you have always eaten in a certain way it will be impossible to change. For some people it will mean making adjustments on many levels, starting in the brain with daily habits, however it will not be impossible. I love the saying 'everything seems impossible until it is done'; in this case maybe it should be ' . . . until you have started'.

I'll say again that this plan is in no way a diet. Dieting is a negative process that feeds off a deprivation mentality. Diets are unsustainable, leading to disordered relationships with food and eating, and – most importantly – they just don't work. They only make us feel worse about ourselves and erode our motivation to try again. Well, this is the last time you will be embarking on a new routine, because this routine is for the rest of your life. It will simply become 'how you live' and 'how you eat', not how you are eating for a week or a month. It will become part of who you are – that's when positive change is lasting.

Plant-based, real-food living is not a quick fix (although you will start noticing positive changes very quickly); it is a lifestyle, a way of living, a new relationship with food and a new approach to eating forever. I am so grateful to have the opportunity to share my story, my beliefs and my recipes, and I thank every one of you for joining this journey towards wellness with me.

Calgary

01
plant-powered living:

why plants will make you feel amazing

o put it simply, plant-powered living involves nothing more than filling your plate with more plants – lots and lots of plants. For some people this can feel daunting, but that's what I am here for – to show you just how easy and accessible this lifestyle can be.

I say 'lifestyle' rather than 'diet' because that is what being plant-based is all about. It isn't simply about adding a few more vegetables to your plate for the next few weeks, nor is it about depriving yourself of anything in order to tick off a certain number of calories or meet a weight-loss target; it is about indulging in all the bountiful and nutritious produce that nature has to offer – now and for the rest of your life. It is also about reshaping your mindset and attitude towards what constitutes 'real' food and embarking upon a new way of thinking when it comes to what you put on your plate each day. When you start and commit to introducing better, real foods into your diet on a daily basis, you will become less reliant or addicted to the 'unreal' options that flood our food retailers (the ones filled with chemicals, additives and flavourings). Most importantly you will feel better and also proud of yourself for taking the steps towards a healthier lifestyle. It is one of the most fulfilling changes you can ever make; once you start, you won't want to look back. When I tell people that they can completely change their life by transitioning to a plant-based diet, I often get a few raised eyebrows. But the truth is, you really can. Plant-based living has the power to make you feel healthier, more energetic and more content in your skin. So let me guide you on this wonderful and colourful plant-powered journey.

my plant-based philosophy

Essentially, my plant-based philosophy is about eating *real* foods. It doesn't get more complicated than that. That means fresh, nutritious ingredients that come from the earth – foods that grow in soil, on trees and on bushes, not foods contrived in a factory. To me, a plant-based diet means that you are eating as many plants as you can. You may wonder why I'm saying 'plants' instead of vegetables. It's because, in my mind, the word 'plant' paints a lovely picture of foods that come from the earth's natural resources: fruits, vegetables, grains, nuts, seeds, beans and anything else from the earth that you can think of. A thriving garden or farmers' market bursting with colour and vitality is so beautiful – and that's also how I want your body to feel and your face to look: bursting with colour and vitality. The health benefits of plants are endless . . .

When considering this approach to eating, I always try to think of food writer Michael Pollan's words: 'Don't eat anything your great-grandmother wouldn't recognize as food.' We need to take a step back in time and remember what food used to be like – that's real food. It's all about changing your mindset and rethinking what nourishing food means. I wouldn't be surprised if at this point you are picturing a lettuce leaf every time I say 'plant-based lifestyle' and wondering how on earth this could be a sustainable way of eating. Fear not! Start thinking about black bean burgers, sweet potatoes with guacamole, healthy rainbow fried rice, and kale and tofu enchiladas. Suddenly plants just got more delicious.

I was raised as a vegetarian by very health-conscious parents. They taught me from an early age that food can be powerful fuel, both physically and emotionally, if you choose the right things to put in your body. They also taught me by example that what we put into our body matters. It affects how we feel, how we think and how we look.

I vividly remember picking carrots from the garden with my grandfather and eating them on the spot. I remember making home-made pasta with my dad (he's Italian) and helping my mom make pumpkin chocolate chip cookies, which were my favourite. (Yes, she was even getting some plants in our cookies way back then.) All of these memories were just part of everyday life, but the importance of eating real, home-made food was never lost on me. My mom was a busy lady but still she cooked us dinner every night and we sat as a family around the table, which of course I didn't appreciate at the time, but the value of healthy food soaked in.

This way of thinking is something that has always been a part of my life in one way or another. And now I have found my ideal lifestyle: plant-based, full of good grains and good fats, low in sugar, wheat, gluten and animal protein, but always flexible and never too extreme. It's so important to listen to what your body needs and not be too hard on yourself. Extremism of any kind backfires every time. While I allow flexibility in my diet, I never lose the inherent desire to focus on nutritious, balanced and wholesome ingredients.

Those intense memories of both my mother and father cooking and, more than anything, that love of the kitchen and the focus on mealtimes as 'family time' have stuck with me. Mealtimes should be the core of every family, even if it is just on the weekends, and even better if it is a meal full of healthy foods. I hope those are the memories I create for my children and that they grow up knowing the benefits of leading a plant-based lifestyle and have wonderful memories of real meals.

does it mean turning vegan?

Leading a plant-based lifestyle doesn't mean saying goodbye to some of your favourite meals. It simply means that, as often as possible, your focus is on natural, wholesome foods and on learning to incoporate vegetables into your meals as much as possible. I would never say you have to be vegetarian or vegan in order to be healthy and plant-based. You can lead a plant-based lifestyle and still eat meat, fish and dairy. The key difference between a vegetarian or vegan diet and leading a plant-based way of living is that the former are about excluding certain foods. Being plant-based, however, is defined by what *is* included and by how much goodness you are adding to your diet through nutritious plants.

I should also add that you shouldn't ever think that cutting out meat and fish instantly means you are leading a healthy diet. I know many vegetarians who live on pasta, starches and potatoes – that's anything but a rich, nutrient-dense diet that fuels you with energy and goodness. It is really important to have the right balance in order for plant-based living to have the maximum impact on your health and happiness.

why is it so important?

It's a simple truth: no amount of sugar-free fizzy drink or gluten-free packaged food can give us what the plants that grow from the ground, trees and bushes can. Processed foods consist of refined ingredients, chemicals and often a lot of sugar, all of which fill us with empty calories, give us cravings for more sugar and processed food, and don't give us the nutrients, fibre and antioxidants that plants can. Plants are grown from the sun's energy and I always think about that energy coming directly into us – fuelling our days and our lives; we eat nature's gifts. Without incorporating these foods into our daily diet, we can't expect to be full of energy, vitality and health.

I know this might sound strange, but my goal is for everyone's kitchen and fridge to be full of food that will rot: in other words, real food. Rotting means fresh ingredients, not packaged foods that can spend a lifetime on your shelves in perfect condition. How can food that can be preserved for decades have any positive benefit to us? It's dead. So, instead of focussing on how much easier these kinds of chemical- and sugar-laden foods make our lives (in the short term only), we need to think about what they are giving us. I'm telling you it's nothing except, eventually, obesity and other diseases. And that's not a scare tactic or an exaggeration: the empty and dead calories in processed food make people sick, overweight and unwell. We're a nation growing in size and illness, and yet fresh foods have never been so plentiful, abundant and diverse.

In contrast, research has already proven that eating a low-sugar, unprocessed, plant-based diet has the potential, alongside other lifestyle changes, to lower the risk of heart disease, type 2 diabetes and high blood pressure. Research into plant-based diets has

similarly found them beneficial to living longer lives and reducing body weight. Essentially, a plant-based diet involves a lower intake of cholesterol, animal protein and saturated fat, while also including a higher amount of dietary fibre, folic acid, vitamins C and E, complex carbohydrates, magnesium, carotenoids plus other phytochemicals. I don't want to put too much emphasis on these studies and on all the health benefits – important as they may be to highlighting the positives of plant-based living – because everyone is different and cannot be grouped quite so easily under one health umbrella.

Ultimately, though, the message is clear: eating plants – and lots of them – as part of a balanced diet will greatly benefit your health and your body. And don't forget about dear old Mother Earth. Plant-based diets are much better for the environment too. As an article published in *Scientific American* titled 'How Meat Contributes to Global Warming' explained, the amount of beef that is eaten in a year by the average American creates as much greenhouse gas as driving a car over 2,900 kilometres. Eating less meat not only benefits our carbon footprint but also significantly minimises our global water consumption. A single kilogram of beef requires approximately 15,000 litres of water to produce it, in comparison to just 240 litres of water for a kilo of cabbage. And that's just the beginning . . .

The first step towards changing your lifestyle to a more plant-based focus is simply making the decision to start. Once you have made that choice (simple, wasn't it?), the next step is to change your perspective on what should go on your plate and in what quantities. Don't be too hard on yourself and set ridiculously impossible goals though. Let's be honest, extremism doesn't work, so making a pact with yourself that you will only ever eat steamed green vegetables from now until eternity is not only unrealistic but is sure to end badly – I guarantee it.

To begin with, just have a think about what you currently eat and how many plants you consume in a day or in a week. My challenge to you is this: however many plants you eat each day now (if you don't want to count, that's fine – just take a guess), make it your goal to double your daily intake by next month. Be conscious of looking at every plate in front of you from a plant perspective. Just think: 'How colourful is this plate?' (and I don't mean thanks to food colouring!) and 'How much of it came from the ground?' Over time, our plates have lost their way and plants have become the side dish or the second fiddle to meat, fish and carbohydrates. I want to flip that ratio on its head and reposition plants as the main attraction.

The next step is to reprogramme your mind to think about plants and vegetables first when you make meals. Your mental conversation shouldn't be, 'What vegetables would go well with that chicken breast recipe I want to try?' It should be, 'What complex carbohydrate or lean protein could accompany this delicious assortment of vegetables I am roasting for dinner tonight?' I have a mental picture I can refer to in my mind, and this is how I think about plant-based living at mealtimes. Take a look at the picture opposite for how my plate looks; it is a really helpful guide for how it should be filled.

I'm not just talking about dinner either. Breakfast and lunch matter too and deserve our equal attention; there's a whole chapter devoted to breakfast (see pages 122–33), where you'll find all kinds of tips and ideas on how to pack more plants into your morning meal. If you work in an office or are out and about away from home, lunchtime might mean having to buy a ready-made lunch. These aren't always high on vegetables, and there might be a temptation to wander off your healthy path. Getting more plants into your lunch is so easy if you can spare a bit of time to pack your own – do it the night before if you're in a rush in the morning. And if you are buying your lunch, instead of buying pre-made sandwiches, which are often slathered in mayo and low on veggie content, go to a deli where you can choose what you want.

If you go to a salad bar, don't just use lettuce as a base and then load on the cheeses, marinated salads (which often have a high sugar content) and meats. Make a conscious effort to add five vegetables other than lettuce to your salad: try different combinations and see what you like. And lay off the dressings: stick with extra virgin olive oil, lemon and

VISUALLY PLANNING YOUR MEAL: what your plate should look like

Every time you look down at your plate, think about the plants first – make them the main attraction, then consider the rest of it.

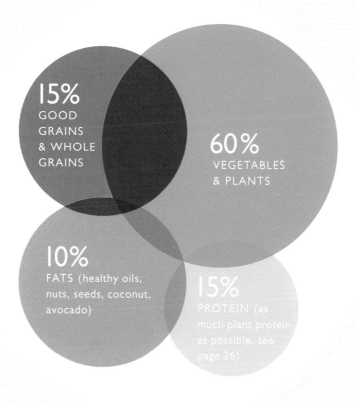

15%
GOOD
GRAINS
& WHOLE
GRAINS

60%
VEGETABLES
& PLANTS

10%
FATS (healthy oils,
nuts, seeds, coconut,
avocado)

15%
PROTEIN (as
much plant protein
as possible, see
page 26)

vinegar. Tamari (gluten-free soy sauce, see page 94) is also great on salads. You can easily buy little secure plastic pots for putting dressing in, so if you know you can't find a nice healthy dressing at the salad bar, just remember to bring a small pot from home and then drizzle it all over your salad when you're back at the office. Or you can keep a bottle of extra virgin olive oil and vinegar in your bottom desk drawer.

Taking a healthy lunch to work, or out and about with you if you're on the go, is one of the best ways to stay on track nutritionally and avoid temptation. Here are some of my favourite packed lunch ideas:

- **Leftovers from your fabulous plant-based dinner are the quickest and easiest way to get your veg in.** Cook extra roasted vegetables, and, if you've got time in the morning, cook some quinoa (see page 70) to mix in with them along with some spinach leaves. Perhaps you had some sweet potatoes (see page 212) for dinner? Again, bake extra then chop them up and mix them with some lettuce, black beans, pine nuts and extra virgin olive oil.

- **Home-made sandwiches take no time at all;** just add veggies, veggies and more veggies between those slices of wholegrain bread. My favourite combinations are avocado, basil and tomatoes, or grilled courgette, pesto, sliced sun-dried tomatoes and rocket.

- **Or use a wholegrain or gluten-free wrap** and fill it with loads of vegetables – raw or cooked – beans, avocado, cheese, tofu or tempeh to make yourself a healthy burrito.

- **Making vegetable soup couldn't be easier.** Sweat your choice of vegetables in a saucepan in extra virgin olive oil with chopped onion and garlic until tender, then cover with vegetable stock or water and a stock cube. Leave to simmer for about 20–35 minutes or until your veggies are soft (the timing varies), then blitz with a hand blender. (To make them extra creamy, try my cashew cream trick on page 80.) If you make a large batch on a Sunday, you can keep returning to it throughout the week to get several portions of wholesome fresh soup for lunch.

- **If you prefer smaller, lighter lunches, just chop up some fresh vegetables** – carrots, broccoli, cucumber, fennel and peppers – and add a dip, such as any of my healthy veggie dip recipes on pages 241–9, or buy some hummus.

what about protein?

When thinking about adopting a plant-based lifestyle, some people might wonder where you're going to get your iron and protein. This is mainly because these are often so heavily associated with animal products and because – wrongly – they're sometimes considered as lacking in a vegetarian diet. Protein plays a crucial role in almost all biological processes so it's a vital part of your diet and around 15–25 per cent of your total calories should come from protein sources. However, contrary to popular belief, these can be easily gained from plants, so this shouldn't be something you feel you are lacking by leading a plant-based lifestyle.

Amino acids are protein's building blocks. Our body is able to produce 13 of the 22 amino acids that make up the proteins we need; it is the remaining nine, known as 'essential amino acids' that we have to find through what we eat. Along with animal proteins, these essential amino acids can be found in a long list of fruits, vegetables, seeds, nuts and legumes. Few contain all nine but as long as you are eating a broad variety of plants as part of your diet, you don't need to be worrying about missing out on protein.

PROTEIN-RICH PLANTS

By knowing which plants are rich in protein, you will soon find yourself loading your plate up with enough to reach your daily requirements. Below is a list of those that are particularly protein-rich. To put these numbers into context, the average adult woman requires 46g of protein per day while the average adult man needs 56g.

01   HEMP SEEDS: around 30g of protein per 100g

02   PEANUT BUTTER: around 29g of protein per 100g

03   ALMONDS/PISTACHIOS: around 21g of protein per 100g

04   TEMPEH: around 21g of protein per 100g

05   CHIA SEEDS: around 20g of protein per 100g

06   WALNUTS/HAZELNUTS: around 15g of protein per 100g

07   EGGS: around 12g of protein per 100g (around 6g in a large egg)

08   GREEK YOGHURT: around 10g of protein per 100g

09   TOFU: around 10g of protein per 100g

10   ADZUKI BEANS: around 7g of protein per 100g of cooked or tinned beans

11   CANNELLINI BEANS: around 7g of protein per 100g of cooked or tinned beans

12   BLACK BEANS: around 6g of protein per 100g of cooked or tinned beans

hazelnuts

03

11

pistachios   cannellini beans

06

walnuts

03   *12*

black beans

almonds

01   *05*

chia seeds

hemp seeds

10

adzuki beans

04

tempeh

07   *09*

eggs   tofu

08

Greek yoghurt

Once you have reshaped your mindset as to how your plate should look, the key is to start integrating more plants into your shopping basket. Some plants may seem familiar while others will no doubt leave you wondering what on earth to do with them. At times it can feel daunting to buy something new and not know what to do with it, but hopefully this book will give you plenty of easy and accessible tips and recipes so that you'll soon be full of ideas for all the amazing options out there.

The key is to be versatile and excited about trying lots of new ingredients – otherwise a diet of nothing more than carrots and broccoli could become pretty bland. I know it is human nature to resort to what we know and are familiar with – I admit, I eat loads of avocados and chickpeas – but I want you to open your eyes to the vast world of vegetables out there. A few years ago, celeriac wasn't part of my vocabulary, yet now I love it and use it in many different ways – from steaming and mashing it, just like mashed potatoes, to shaving it raw into crisp summer salads.

Thinking about what is seasonal can help you on that mission. I have a poster in my kitchen that lists which vegetables are in season throughout the year, and I often glance at it when I'm stuck for ideas. Buying seasonal produce is important because it is less likely to have been shipped around the globe, which both impacts the environment and increases your cost. When crops are transported long distances they have to be harvested early, refrigerated and stored, so they don't ripen as effectively as they would if grown seasonally in a natural environment. This also impacts the flavour and nutrient quality – so your food

YEAR ROUND

AVOCADO	GINGER	THYME
(it's always imported)	LENTILS	TURNIPS
BLACK-EYED PEAS	LETTUCE	YAM
BUTTER BEANS	MUSHROOMS	
CABBAGE	ONIONS	
CARROTS	PAK CHOI	
CELERY	PARSLEY	
CHARD	PEPPERS	
CHICKPEAS	POTATOES	
CHIVES	SEAWEED	
CORIANDER	SHALLOTS	
CUCUMBER	SPINACH	
DILL	SPRING ONIONS	
GARLIC	SQUASH	

tastes better and is better for you if it's meant to be eaten in that season. And, no matter where you live, most people have access to a plethora of vegetables all year round. There is always so much more available beyond carrots and celery . . . so no more excuses please! When you do your next shop, open up your imagination to everything on offer and why not try something new? Here's a list to look over, learn, tear out of the book, scribble on, stick on your fridge, photocopy, scan, and keep in your bag for when you go shopping. You know what I am saying – use it. Put a tick next to the fruit and vegetables you've tried cooking with and a star next to the ones you plan to try in the next few months. Once you've got over the hurdle of 'I don't like X' or 'I don't know how to cook with Y', it will just become part of your routine to put that plant into your basket. And you don't need to buy everything on this list in your first shop – in fact, please don't, otherwise you will be cursing me as your kitchen overflows with food that will rot.

I have a poster in my kitchen that lists which vegetables are in season throughout the year – your food tastes better and is better for you if it's meant to be eaten in that season.

SPRING AND SUMMER	AUTUMN AND WINTER
ASPARAGUS	BEETROOT
AUBERGINE	BROCCOLI
BASIL	BRUSSELS SPROUTS
COURGETTE	CAULIFLOWER
FENNEL	CELERIAC
GREEN BEANS	CURLY ENDIVE
PEAS	HORSERADISH
RADISH	JERUSALEM ARTICHOKE
ROCKET	KALE
RUNNER BEANS	LEEKS
SPRING GREENS	PARSNIPS
SUGAR SNAP PEAS	PUMPKIN
TOMATOES	SWEDE
WATERCRESS	SWEET POTATOES

Organic food is anything agricultural that has been grown and processed according to a strict set of rules. To be organic, the soil must be safe, there must have been no modifications to the food product, it must not have been exposed to synthetic pesticides, petroleum or sewage-based fertilisers, and it must not have been genetically modified. You are lucky if you are able to buy all of the plants from the list above from nearby farms or can easily make organic choices. For most though, this can prove to be costly and isn't always feasible. Therefore, it is important to understand that some plants are affected more drastically by the pollution in soil than others – meaning they absorb more of the bad stuff farmers put on their crops. Opposite is my list of the 'filthy fifteen' – the foods that you should try to buy as organic whenever you can for this reason. It is also worth remembering the 'clean fifteen', which are the fruit and vegetables that absorb the fewest pesticides, and therefore can in theory be bought non-organically. The list changes annually, although it generally retains the same key names.

Although my book doesn't really cover meat and fish, I should add here that buying organic free-range meat and dairy products should be your first priority. Often, what we don't think about is what the animals we eat are eating. In the same way that we don't want to fill our bodies with chemicals, neither should we want their bodies pumped with them either. When those chemicals are absorbed into an animal's body, they also filter into the produce we eat, whether that is their meat, their milk or their eggs. For livestock to be considered organic, it must be given organic feed, have access to the outdoors, cannot be given antibiotics, animal by-products or growth hormones, and the soil must have been free from fertilisers for a set period of time. So if you're buying eggs, dairy and other animal products, organic is definitely the best option wherever possible.

Whenever serving guests or family something new or 'adventurous' don't tell them what it is until they've said 'this is delicious', which I'm sure they will. This way, over time, you are changing people's perceptions of how amazing plant-based eating can be without coming up against too much disagreement. One mouthful at a time!

THE FILTHY FIFTEEN

- Apples
- Celery
- Cherry tomatoes
- Chilli peppers
- Cucumber
- Grapes
- Kale
- Nectarines
- Peaches
- Peppers
- Potatoes
- Spinach
- Spring greens
- Strawberries
- Sugar snap peas

THE CLEAN FIFTEEN

- Asparagus
- Aubergine
- Avocado
- Cabbage
- Cantaloupe melon
- Cauliflower
- Grapefruit
- Kiwi
- Mangoes
- Onions
- Papaya
- Petit pois *(frozen)*
- Pineapple
- Sweetcorn
- Sweet potatoes

plant-based parenting

I have three kids so I know getting children to eat more vegetables isn't always easy. However, I firmly believe that kids weren't programmed in utero just to eat white pasta and breaded chicken. Wherever you are on your journey to get more vegetables inside your kids, below are a few tricks I use (or maybe I should say 'tactics' – but in all honesty, don't feel guilty about tricking them!) And for lots more tips on eating healthily with kids, turn to the Family chapter on page 134.

01   The first thing I put down on the table – when they are at their hungriest – is a plate of raw veggies cut up with a dip (see pages 241–49). Or, if there isn't time for that, I separate their meal into two plates and serve the one with vegetables first. Yes, you have to wash two plates, but it does make a difference serving the veggies when their appetite is highest.

02   I don't just use tomatoes when making a pasta sauce for my family. The beauty of puréeing sauces is that you can't actually tell what is in them, and the more veggies you add, the more delicious they taste. Try adding roasted, sautéed or steamed carrots, courgettes, peppers or fennel to your basic tomato sauce. They won't change its colour drastically, but they will bring plenty of added flavour and nutrition.

03   This may already be happening in your kitchen if you have a baby, but if not start batch-making purées of veggies like courgette, pumpkin, butternut squash, broccoli, carrots, cauliflower, sweet potatoes, spinach, beetroot and peas, then freeze in small portions so you only have to defrost what you need for cooking or baking.

04   Think of fun names for each of your plant-based meals to keep children entertained and come up with interesting ways to present them too. For example, I always give my children chopped celery with almond butter in the middle and chia seeds sprinkled on the top. We call this 'ants on a log', which they love. Or we have half an avocado filled with balsamic vinegar and extra virgin olive oil and call it 'a capsizing boat' – with toothpicks as the oars, of course.

05   Have a Mexican-themed night and make burritos. Put out bowls of fillings – I like black beans, cheese, quinoa, diced avocado and tomatoes – then get the kids to make their own. The rule is they have to include at least four choices before they can roll it up.

06   Some batters you are making or using (pancake and muffin batters tend to be easiest) can be supplemented with veggie purées. The easiest to sneak in are: spinach, courgette, sweet potato, carrots, pumpkin, beetroot and butternut squash – try my beetroot buckwheat pancakes on page 164.

07   You can also add many different puréed and chunky veggies into veggie burgers (see my black bean burgers on page 208).

02
getting organised:
simple steps for healthy living

Imagine this . . . You wake up in the morning, walk downstairs, open your fridge door and find a large bowl of chia seed pudding or Bircher muesli ready for your breakfast, plus home-made broccoli meatballs, already rolled and waiting to be popped in the oven for your dinner the minute you get home. Then you open your freezer and find spinach and kale separated out in portion-sized bags, washed and ready to be added to your smoothies; or banana and pecan muffins, waiting to be defrosted for a tasty after-school or work snack.

Sounds pretty great, right? So let's make this weekly food plan a reality. Think of me as your kitchen therapist. Little by little, step by step, I am going to help you create new habits and restock your life in a new and very organised way. It may not happen overnight or without bumps along the way, but in the end, I promise you, the journey to a cleaner and greener kitchen will be worth it.

I like to think about food the same way I think about people. You don't want to populate your life with people who zap your energy or focus on the negative, do you? Life is exponentially better when you surround yourself with friends and colleagues who boost and inspire you to feel and do better. The same should go for the food with which you keep company. Just like having optimistic people around you, the more you fill your surroundings with positive, nutritious, wholesome foods, the better off you will be. By the end of this chapter, my hope is that you will be sat with pen and paper in hand, starting to plan your meals, fill your online shopping basket and ready to organise your kitchen and revolutionise your cooking.

First, let's make your cupboards and drawers work for you, not against you. You should be able to reach in at any time and come up with something that will fuel your body and mind with nutritional goodness. And the key is *getting organised*.

ducks in a row: making your plan

In a chapter about organisation and planning, it may come as no surprise that the first thing I am going to suggest we do together is make a step-by-step plan containing a few simple and straightforward ideas that will, when put into action, make a healthy diet and lifestyle seem a lot more achievable. I find it always helps to turn your overall goal into smaller, more manageable, bite-sized chunks. I don't want this to feel regimented or overwhelming, so I have tried to make things as simple as possible. Hopefully the strategies in this chapter will be a reassuring reference when you feel like you might be veering off track or just need some structure to reach your goals. I guarantee you that a little bit of planning and organisation is key to your success.

Mentally, I separate my kitchen into three distinct worlds. These fall quite simply under the headings of fridge, freezer and pantry (the latter gets a whole chapter devoted to it – turn to page 60 to find out all about your pantry staples). As we know, it is very important to have fresh, nutritious produce (plants) accessible to you and your family all week long. With this in mind, the fridge – home to the majority of these delicious ingredients – needs the most frequent consideration, so let's begin there.

FRIDGE CHECK

Every week I set aside some time – 10 minutes maximum – to think about: how many meals we'll be eating at home that week and how many will be eaten out; how many kids' lunches I need to pack; and how many days I will be bringing lunch into work with me. If you do this, then you can think clearly about what you actually need for the week ahead.

Start by going through your fridge to check what is already in there. Throw away anything that has gone off and generally organise it if you find it's looking a bit messy – a clean, orderly fridge is far more motivating and a lot less overwhelming than a chaotic one. I am always surprised by the things I find hiding behind a carton of milk. I usually do a quick inventory of my freezer and cupboards at the same time to keep tabs on what is running low. Now you are ready to decide what to cook for the days to come.

PRIORITISE

When it comes to planning meals, start by choosing recipes that will use up the ingredients you already have. This is why it's important to know what's in your fridge. As you sketch out your food options for the week, order the meals so that any ingredients that need eating soon will get used first.

So say I have a bag of spinach that is rapidly wilting, I would make sure that my first meal of the week included it – for example scrambled eggs and spinach (see page 172). Or perhaps a few tired leeks and a couple of sweet potatoes can be blitzed into a healthy soup stirred with cashew cream (see page 80) for extra richness. And if all else fails and you're struggling to incorporate ingredients in your cooking immediately, you can simply throw them in your freezer for later (see pages 50–8 for what can be frozen and how best to freeze them).

LOVELY LISTS

Once you have taken stock of what is currently in your fridge, cupboards and freezer, then it's time to write out a shopping list. This should contain everything missing from your kitchen that is required for making each meal on your plan and to generally stock your fridge for the week. However, as fresh vegetables and fruit can sometimes go out of date quicker than you can eat them, unless you're planning on freezing things it is best to only ever buy what you know you will be able to eat in the time between your stock-up days. No one likes wasting food or money.

Having a shopping list helps you avoid putting spontaneous – and often less healthy – purchases in your basket. It also means you are able to see where ingredients overlap for different recipes to ensure you aren't buying too much of one thing. I find it is really helpful to write my shopping list in the same order as the ingredients are stocked where I shop, so I am not going back and forth every five minutes while shopping. I list all the fresh fruit and vegetables together, all the canned items, all the dairy, condiments, etc. and it helps me stay focussed and ensure nothing is missed. I also put a star next to anything I want try to buy as organic, using my list of the filthy fifteen (see page 31) as a guide.

However, if you haven't written a specific meal plan or, as we all do, find yourself going to the shops without recipe inspiration in mind for the week ahead, then I find it is always handy to carry a master list of quick 'good-for-you and useful' ingredient ideas to pick and choose from. Seeing the words 'butternut squash' or 'Portobello mushroom' will hopefully prompt a meal idea. I always rely on my staple star dishes that are locked in my memory – the ones I know I can make with my eyes closed that the whole family likes – and that's most often my Rainbow fried rice on page 198. If all else fails, it's great to have as a fallback. Another great tip if you're short on time is to use your phone to take a quick photo of the inside of your fridge before you leave the house. That way, you'll be able to take quick stock of everything you have when you're on the move.

HEADING TO THE SHOPS

It is important to create a routine to your planning that works for you. I like to set aside specific days of the week that I mark as food shopping days so I can get into a shopping rhythm. For me this is Saturday or Sunday and Wednesday or Thursday, but you must find the times of the week that work best for you. Maybe you always have a meeting at the end of every Tuesday that is near a great market, or perhaps on Saturday mornings your kids go to football for an hour and you can sneak off to the grocery store. It doesn't matter what days you choose as long as they allow you the time that you need to shop with as little stress as possible.

When you do head to the shops, take your rough meal plan and ingredients list with you. If you haven't had a chance to write up either of these, take a picture of a recipe from a cookbook with your phone or tag specific ideas from apps on your phone that you want to try. This way you will whizz through the store more efficiently, and won't find yourself buying less healthy options spontaneously in a moment of 'I have no idea what to make!' It is also a good idea to be well fuelled when making a run to the store – shopping on an empty tummy is never a good thing, and supermarkets have a number of tricks up their sleeves to get you to buy more rubbish. So go with a plan and stick to it. The same applies to online shopping. I have a set 'basket' that is full of things I always seem to buy, and then I can quickly add and delete from there. This not only saves a lot of time but it limits the amount of browsing I may be tempted to do for new ice cream flavours.

writing lists with little ones

Get kids involved in writing the master list and have them try to think of all the healthy fruits and vegetables they can name. For those items on your list that they've never heard of, make a plan to try out one new ingredient per week together and figure out what to make with it. Try to keep it varied and interesting. Once you've given it a go, tick it off the list. It will most likely expand your knowledge of healthy foods just as much as it will broaden theirs.

the power of the prep day

Once you have shopped, the most important step comes into play, and that is cracking on with all your 'prep day' activities. In the same way that it is important to set aside time for shopping, it is also important to allow time in your schedule for prepping everything you buy. A prep day is essentially what the name suggests: getting everything ready in your kitchen for the week ahead to save you time and effort in the long run. We all lead such busy lives these days, so rather than spending time each night making individual meals, you can get a lot prepared ahead in one go and in large batches to then use throughout the rest of the week.

When I say 'prep day', I don't want you to imagine you have to block out a whole day to spend time slaving over the stove and sweating over what to cook. I just mean that you choose a day that works best for you and allot as much time as you can. For my family it's Sunday, but there's no magic to that day. At most I set aside an hour and a half to do my prep, and sometimes it is much less than that.

Choose which day or days are right for you depending on your work and commitments, and make it part of your regular schedule. That's why I think it's helpful to give it a name – prep day – so that it becomes part of your weekly routine. Of course, if you'd rather, you can be fluid and switch days, but personally I find it is easier to get into a consistent habit. You can also break your prep day down into smaller chunks throughout your week or weekend and get as much done as possible by grouping tasks together. For example, if you are making breakfast on a Sunday morning that involves chopping fruit, then why not chop a bit extra and pop it in a bowl in the fridge? You can use it for smoothies, to throw on yoghurt and granola or just to have ready as an afternoon snack. Or, if you're making scrambled egg and spinach, why not whisk up twice as much mixture and pop the other half in the fridge ready for Monday morning? The same applies for pancake batter – you can always make a double batch and keep it in the fridge to use later in the week – who's going to refuse pancakes twice in one week?

Once you get in the prep-day habit, you'll be amazed by how much time it saves you to have basics and meal-bases ready for the week ahead. Suddenly a meal that would have taken up a chunk of your evening will take only 10 minutes to create. I've given you lots of ideas for your chosen prep day throughout this chapter – some are specifically for your fridge and some are for your freezer. You don't have to do all of them, and some are going to be more relevant than others depending on your meal plan, but how about trying one new idea each week and see how it works for you?

forget the boil
The one thing that destroys much of the nutritional goodness in vegetables is cooking them in too much water (aka boiling). Steaming or roasting your choices is best and retains more of their nutritional value. When steaming, only cook vegetables until they are tender (not mushy but 'al dente', as the Italians say — a bit crunchy and still retaining their vibrant colour).

prep-day staple: lentils

Lentils make a wonderful base to any healthy meal. Cook a big batch (400–500g) of my perfect lentils on your prep day then store them in the fridge and use them in my four lentil recipes – four ways with one simple ingredient.

lentils four ways...

1. Add the cooked lentils to a soup or stew to bulk it out.

2. Make a simple yet filling halloumi and lentil salad (see page 186 and photo opposite).

3. For a quick Middle Eastern salad, bake some aubergine in thin slices with extra virgin olive oil, salt and pepper on top (preheat the oven to 240°C/ gas 9 and cook for 20–30 minutes depending on the thickness of the slices). Then chop the aubergine, add it to lentils and top it all with a tahini dressing (see page 247).

4. Whizz the lentils into a lentil and red onion dip (see page 244) for vegetable dippers, or use as side for fish or lean meat.

||||||||||||||||||||||||||||||||||||||||||||||||||||||||||

HOW TO COOK PERFECT LENTILS

• Check the cooking time on the packet — it differs depending on the type. Yellow and red split lentils take 15–20 minutes, while green and brown lentils can take up to 45. If you have had the lentils in the cupboard for a while, they will also take longer than normal.

• You don't have to soak lentils first, but doing so reduces their cooking time by about half. Always rinse them in cold water to clean off debris and pick out any shrivelled lentils, then drain.

• Pour them into a medium saucepan and cover with two to three times their volume in water.

• Add a bay leaf to the pan if you have one and place over a medium–high heat. Bring the water to a boil, before reducing the temperature to maintain a gentle simmer and cover with the lid. Continue cooking in this way, ensuring that the water level doesn't go below the lentils. Add more hot water to the pan if necessary.

• Towards the end, once you think the lentils are softening, season with some salt. Don't add this too early, otherwise it will be neutralised by the cooking and you will have to add more to achieve the same flavour.

• Once cooked, remove the pan from the heat and leave to sit with the lid on for 5–10 minutes. This helps make the lentils juicier as they absorb more water, though it's not essential. Drain and they're ready to use.

||||||||||||||||||||||||||||||||||||||||||||||||||||||||||

ideas for your fridge prep day

01   Wash all your greens and vegetables thoroughly.

02   Chop up your greens – kale, spinach, Swiss chard, etc. – so they are ready to be added to stir-fries, salads, soups, smoothies, breakfast, etc.

03   Chop up half of the carrots, celery and fennel you have bought, and any other similar crudité-type vegetables, so they are ready to eat as snacks, take to work, dip in hummus or put in the kids' lunches. Keep them in Tupperware boxes in the fridge and they will stay crisp for two days.

04   For salad, once washed, strip the leaves from the lettuce but keep the pieces whole and just put them in an airtight bag with a damp paper towel – you can rip them apart or chop them right before you are going to use them.

05   Hard-boil some eggs so they are ready for snacks (see opposite).

06   Soak almonds (see page 74 for how to do this). You can eat them as snacks, blitz them into almond butter (see page 80 for my recipe) or chop them and add to muesli, granola or porridge. You could also use these to prepare some home-made almond milk (see page 78). When stored in the fridge in a tightly sealed container and shaken before use, almond milk will last for up to five days.

07   Make some overnight oats (see page 159) so you have them for the following two days.

08   Soak then cook some dried beans or chickpeas. These will be helpful to add in to your salads, some of your meals or, in the case of chickpeas, roasted as snacks (see page 219 for my tamari ginger roasted chickpeas).

09   Toast some pine nuts, pistachios and almonds to add to salads, quinoa or your breakfast. Keep them in the fridge once they're cooled.

10   Deseed a pomegranate to use throughout the week in porridge, muesli or on top of salads.

11   Prepare a few dips (sees pages 241–49) to have with raw veggies, oatcakes or rice cakes throughout the week.

12   Roast some vegetables – these are as delicious eaten cold as leftovers.

prep-day staple: eggs

Hard-boiled eggs are a really handy ingredient to have in your fridge. Cook a big batch (see below for how I cook mine) and then store them in Tupperware boxes (peeled or unpeeled) in the fridge. They make a really easy snack or can be added to salads and lunch boxes for a healthy dose of protein.

‖‖‖‖‖‖‖‖‖‖‖‖‖‖‖‖‖‖‖‖‖‖‖‖‖‖‖‖‖‖‖‖

HOW TO COOK PERFECT HARD-BOILED EGGS

• Fill a medium-sized saucepan with enough water to cover the eggs by 4–5cm.

• Place the eggs in the pan and heat the water over a high heat until it begins to boil.

• At this point, cover the pan with a lid and turn the heat down to low, then cook for another minute.

• Remove from the heat and leave covered for around 10 minutes before draining the water.

• Rinse the eggs under cold water continuously for 1 minute, then peel once they're cool enough to handle or store them in their shells.

‖‖‖‖‖‖‖‖‖‖‖‖‖‖‖‖‖‖‖‖‖‖‖‖‖‖‖‖‖‖‖‖

you can...

1. Throw together an easy salad with green leaves, olives, chopped peppers and sliced onions, then top with sliced hard-boiled eggs.

2. Create a twist on a cold kedgeree, by adding an egg to my curried wild rice salad (see page 185).

3. If your kids are adept at peeling them, pop them in their lunch box with the shells on. If not, peel them and place them in a plastic bag with a pinch of salt and pepper.

4. Serve a quick and easy appetiser of curried devilled eggs. Carefully remove the yolks from 6 hard-boiled eggs and mash them. Mix with chopped pickles, capers, a little extra virgin olive oil and white wine vinegar, and some mustard and curry powder. Spoon the mixture back into the whites, or mash the whites too and try it on top of gluten-free toast or crackers.

5. Slice or chop an egg to add extra protein to avocado on toast (see page 175).

get savvy with spinach

Spinach is one of my all-time favourite vegetables – it's so handy as it can be used at every mealtime and I'll always have a load in both my fridge and freezer. Here are some ways you can add it to your meals:

Wash the leaves then mix them through salads, whole or chopped (see pages 183 and 188 for a couple of sugggestions where this would work well).

Sprinkle finely chopped raw spinach on top of pasta and soups.

When making your morning scrambled eggs (see page 172), add chopped spinach. Add it when stirring your eggs in the pan. It will quickly wilt. Fast, delicious and easy.

You can include spinach in black bean burgers (see page 208 for my recipe). Either wilt it in a frying pan and add to the burger mixture, or lay the washed leaves on top of your burger once it has been cooked as part of the filling.

Spinach makes a delicious side dish for any meat or fish. Simply steam it for 2–3 minutes (with the lid off) until it has wilted down but is still bright green, then season with salt, pepper, lemon and a drizzle of extra virgin olive oil for added flavour.

To instantly supercharge a smoothie (see page 177), add a handful of spinach (or two, if you're feeling particularly green). Simply wash and use fresh – no need to cook. It will whizz down instantly and kiddies especially will never even know it is there.

Take your children shopping with you and get them to pick three plants they want to try. Then you can come up with exciting ways to cook them together. When they are involved in the whole process, it will make it much more fun and exciting for them.

befriend your freezer

Once you feel like your fridge is well on its way to being organised, you can turn your attention to your freezer. Let me introduce you to your new best friend. Most people don't realise what a fabulous ally their freezer can be in the quest to eat well – it can be hugely instrumental in helping you stay organised, de-stressed and nutritionally on track. And unlike your fridge, which demands your attention regularly, your freezer is a little less high maintenance. All it needs is a bit of dedicated love and attention every few weeks – or even just once a month. Then you can add to it as and when throughout the week, should you find yourself with any leftovers or wilting ingredients.

My mission is to get you to use your freezer. It always bums me out when I go to a friend's house and all I see in the freezer is ice and maybe a freezer-burned carton of ice cream. Your freezer can be a saviour on super-busy days when you have that 'uh-oh' moment and find that there is nothing in the fridge. My dream is to have everyone's freezer bursting with healthy food options for breakfast, lunch or dinner and organised in such a way that finding what to have is really simple and straightforward.

You can freeze specific ingredients so that all you have to do is quickly defrost them and add to a simple dinner plan. Alternatively, you can freeze leftovers of any favourite dishes that you've made so that you can enjoy them another time.

Your freezer can be a saviour on super-busy days when you have that 'uh-oh' moment and find that there is nothing in the fridge.

I hope you finish this chapter brimming with ideas and inspiration on all the wonderful ingredients that you can freeze effectively and how this can help you implement a new way of eating. For example, did you know that you can freeze cooked rice and quinoa, cooked beans, legumes, nuts, bread, fish and lightly steamed vegetables? You can also freeze pancake batter, greens such as spinach and kale, herbs, avocado (which is helpful given how quickly these can go from unripe to mushy), citrus juice and even pesto (you just have to add the cheese after you defrost). And frozen bananas are great to add to smoothies in the morning to give them a fabulous taste and thick and creamy texture (my kids call it 'ice-creamy').

Equally as important as knowing what you can freeze is knowing what you can't freeze so that you don't end up with soggy, crumbly, tasteless meals. In general, a good rule is to avoid freezing anything with a high water content, but, more specifically, steer clear from freezing cheese, whole eggs, cooked pasta, sauces made with flour, salad, celery and certain fruits like grapefruit and watermelon. Check out my full lists opposite and on page 57.

Ultimately, befriending your freezer will help you make healthier choices and avoid stress on busy days. If you know in the back of your mind that you have a delicious pasta sauce, a marinated chicken breast, vegetables to add to an omelette or a savoury muffin ready to be defrosted and eaten in minutes, eating healthily suddenly feels more manageable. With the help of your freezer, preparing healthy meals is anything but slow; it's the kind of fast food I like.

freezing fruit and vegetables

When you buy fresh fruit and vegetables they will, of course, go bad. Sometimes this happens very quickly, which can make eating healthily seem like a chore – and expensive. But if you use your freezer effectively, it won't be an issue. Knowing what does and doesn't freeze is key, so here is an at-a-glance list to keep on hand when buying and storing.

Most fruits keep well for 6 months but always check their odour and appearance before eating.

apples
apricots
avocados *(I usually peel and cut mine into segments before freezing)*
bananas *(peeled)*
berries
cherries *(stoned)*
cranberries
grapes
peaches *(stoned)*
pears
pineapple
tomatoes *(cooked)*

Blanch most vegetables quickly before freezing. Most keep well for 6 months, but check odour and appearance before eating.

asparagus
beetroot
broccoli
carrots
cauliflower
courgettes
green beans
leafy greens *(raw)*
mushrooms
okra
onions *(raw)*
peas
peppers and chillies *(raw)*
spinach and other hardy greens
squashes and pumpkin
sweetcorn

grapefruit
oranges *(unless you want to serve them frozen)*
strawberries *(because of their high water content)*
tomatoes *(raw)*
watermelon

beansprouts
Brussels sprouts
cabbage
celery
cress
cucumber
lettuce and other salad leaves
potatoes
radishes

If you throw all your berries, fruit chunks or chopped greens in a bag together and put them in the freezer, they will become one big clump and are essentially unusable – unless you are handy with an ice pick. Using the technique below means that you can reach in and easily get a nice handful of whatever you need, whenever you need it. This is especially ideal when making your morning smoothies or quickly getting snacks for your children to have after school. It also helps for eating foods when they are out of season. By freezing extra when they are ripe, ready and available, they will be there for you to use later in the year.

Wash your fruit or greens thoroughly. Peel bananas and chop fruit such as apples, bananas, pears, peaches and pineapple. For greens, chop them into small pieces. You can remove the stalks of kale if you want, but you don't have to – especially if you plan to use these greens in smoothies, in which case everything will be pulverised anyway.

Line a baking tray with parchment paper and spread a single layer of greens, berries or banana pieces, or whatever you decide to freeze, over the paper.

Put the baking tray in your freezer overnight.

The next day remove the ingredients from the sheet and put them in plastic freezer bags. Label each bag with what is inside.

how to freeze herbs

Freezing herbs can make them go brown and limp. To avoid this, you can either brush them with olive oil before placing them in a freezer bag to freeze them or — even better, especially for hard herbs like rosemary, sage, thyme and oregano — you can preserve them by freezing them in ice cubes of olive oil. Either chop the herbs finely or leave them in larger sprigs and leaves. (You can freeze individual herbs or make combinations of finely chopped and whole herbs, such as rosemary, fennel stalk, sage and oregano.) Pack the wells of ice cube trays about two-thirds full of herbs, then pour extra virgin olive oil over them. Cover the trays lightly with cling film and freeze overnight. Remove the frozen cubes and store in small bags. Label each bag with the type of herb or herbs inside.

freezer fantastic

Now you've become reacquainted with your freezer, here are my top tips on how to use it safely and most efficiently, so you always have healthy options at the ready.

01 Be sure to label every container or bag with details of its contents and the date it needs to be removed from the freezer. Ingredients will keep for different amounts of time and you need to be careful of this, so check out my guidelines on page 57.

02 Cool all soups, stews, sauces before freezing.

03 Steam or blanch vegetables briefly before freezing. When foods are frozen, their enzyme action is slowed, but not stopped. Blanching destroys or inactivates food's enzyme action and reduces your risk of food poisoning.

04 Freeze foods in individual portion sizes so that you can defrost the amount you need and nothing goes to waste.

05 Once everything is in the freezer, make sure there is enough space for the air to circulate. Remember to use the oldest items first (see, the labels do come in handy!).

06 Don't refreeze things once you have defrosted them. Every time a product is frozen its cell walls are ruptured in the process, and when you refreeze foods after they've already been thawed even more cellular structure is destroyed, making them lose flavour and taste and giving bacteria a chance to develop.

07 Place all frozen meat and fish in the bottom section of your freezer. This is important as it means nothing below them will be contaminated should they happen to leak. It is particularly important that these have dates on them and that you should always eat the oldest first, rotating them regularly.

How you store frozen food is important so that foods retain their flavour and vitality for as long as possible. Also, you don't want flavours and smells seeping and mixing in the freezer – no one likes berries that smell or taste like pesto. Here are the items that are really useful to have in your cupboards to make freezer organisation and storage simple and successful. Always use BPA–free plastic and glass containers to prevent chemicals leaching into your food.

- PLASTIC FREEZER BAGS: Good for freezing chopped fruit and greens – just make sure you follow my step-by-step guide on page 52 so they don't clump together.

- TUPPERWARE BOXES: Good for freezing soups and sauces. (Don't forget to let them cool first though.)

- CLING FILM: Good for wrapping portions of cooked food.

- SHALLOW PLASTIC TUBS (NO LID): Good to store anything wrapped in cling film to prevent any leaks or spillages contaminating other food items.

- ICE-LOLLY MOULDS: Good for smoothies (see page 177) and juices to turn them into healthy lollies.

- ICE CUBE TRAYS: Good for storing portions of pesto or herbs.

By this point, I hope you are feeling that eating real food is all a bit more manageable than when we first began. You now have a step-by-step plan for creating your menu, buying your ingredients and getting everything that you will need to go in your fridge ready for the week ahead. Preparing your fresh ingredients in advance really does take the pressure off you mid-week, and I'm all about eliminating any panic when it comes to eating healthily. It is definitely worth the 30 minutes–1½ hours (or as long as you can spare on your prep day) to have a week full of healthy, wholesome, stress-free eating.

So when you get home, turn on some music, open your fridge door and take your pick. It is important to ease your mind so that you can focus on other things or just relax a bit.

what to freeze

Not everything freezes well and even things that do have a freezer shelf life. Here's a guide to some of the things that keep best – they're what you'll most likely find in my freezer at any given moment.

HEALTHY FOODS THAT FREEZE WELL

- Beans (when soaked, keep for up to 3 months; when cooked, keep for 6 months)
- Cooked lean meat, such as chicken, pork or beef (keep for up to 3 months)
- Cooked lentils (keep for up to 3 months)
- Cooked quinoa (keeps for 1 to 2 months)
- Cooked rice (keeps for up to 3 months)
- Fish, cooked and uncooked (will keep for up to 3 months)
- Hardy herbs, such as rosemary, oregano, sage or thyme (these keep for up to one year)
- Peanuts and nuts such as pine nuts, walnuts, brazil nuts, hazelnuts, almonds, cashew nuts, macadamia nuts, pecans and shelled pistachios (most keep well for 6 months but always check odour and appearance before eating)
- Pancake batter (keeps for up to 1 month)
- Pesto, without the cheese (most keep well for 3–6 months but always check the odour and appearance before eating; see page 241 for my recipes)
- Raw meat (keeps for up to 3 months)
- Raw separated eggs (keep for up to 3 months)
- Soups (most keep well for 3–6 months)
- Tomato sauce (most keep for 3–6 months but check the odour and appearance before eating; see page 202 for recipe)

BUT DON'T FREEZE . . .

- Cheese – it becomes soggy once thawed.
- Raw eggs in their shells – the shells expand in the freezer and crack.
- Cooked egg – it will become tough and rubbery.
- Yoghurt – it will separate and become lumpy.
- Pasta sauces made with cornflour or flour – they will separate and become lumpy.
- Spices – their flavour changes during freezing.
- Cooked wholegrain pasta – it becomes mushy when frozen and thawed.
- Anything in a can or jar – the contents expand and may cause the container to explode.

01   Cook portions of quinoa and rice, then let them cool and put them in individual clear plastic bags before freezing. I usually put enough for two people in each bag and mark how many portions I've stored on the label.

02   Cook lentils and beans, then freeze them in small, usable batches.

03   Freeze berries and other fruit (see page 52 for how best to do this).

04   Wash, chop and freeze greens: kale or spinach for smoothies; Swiss chard or pak choi for a stir-fry.

05   Make two simple pasta sauces (for example, one of my pesto recipes, see page 241, and my tomato sauce, see page 202) and put them into individually portioned freezer bags.

06   Freeze grapes as a fun and healthy treat for kids or to pop in to drinks as tasty and refreshing ice cubes.

07   Make vegan ice cream (see page 237) as a treat to enjoy later in the week.

08   Cook a large batch of vegan lasagne (see page 215). Once cooled, slice into portions, wrap individually in cling film and pop in the freezer. These can be pulled out and reheated to eat with a fresh salad on busy days.

09   If you eat meat and fish, you can wash, prep, marinate (if you like to) and portion out your protein, then wrap it in cling film and pop in your freezer. Remember to put your meat and fish in the bottom drawer of your freezer in case the portions leak.

10   Make a batch of muffins (see page 223) or cookies (see page 227) to freeze, then defrost them as you need them. They make a great snack during homework time.

03

pantry staples:
how to fill your cupboards with goodness

by now you will have shopped for your wholesome, vibrant plants. To turn them into balanced nutritious meals, they're even more wonderful when cooked alongside grains, seeds, legumes, nuts and spices. This is where a well-stocked, healthy pantry comes in.

I don't know what it's like in your house, but in mine busy schedules and kiddie chaos mean there just isn't always time to go out and buy all the ingredients I might need to make a recipe there and then. Making last-minute runs to the grocery store or supermarket is at best difficult, at worst impossible. However healthy cooking will never feel like a chore if all you need to do is reach in the cupboard for good-quality staples. Having a pantry that complements your plant-based lifestyle will unquestionably save you heaps of time and stress in the long run, and the amount of meals you will be able to whip up at the drop of a hat will astound you.

Throughout this chapter I am going to list and explain all of my favourite – and often downright essential – pantry items. These are my hero products that I find myself using on a regular basis and that feature in my recipes too. I promise that I won't be encouraging you to fill your cupboards with anything that is going to sit on your shelves and gather dust; my suggestions are things that I want you to use on a regular basis and that you will no doubt find yourself naturally restocking in your efforts to maintain a healthy pantry. Think of me as the spring cleaner of your shelves, ready to help you whip them into a well-behaved, organised order. The key is that everything you fill your cupboards with is 'real' and that the ingredients help you on your path to a more plant-based lifestyle.

My goal is that you finish this chapter feeling excited – not daunted – about shopping for ingredients that might be new to you, as well as brimming with practical ideas for how to use each one. Soon you will see just how much it can change your eating habits to have a revolutionised pantry.

I have divided my staples into groups. Within these sections, I've listed items in alphabetical order, rather than in the order I love them. You should, by no means, feel you need to buy everything on each list. Take your time to fill your cupboards – remember that starting and committing to change is the most important step. If you want to revamp everything all in one go, then that's great, but it's equally okay to set a three-month goal to make these changes over time or simply according to your tastes and needs. Maybe try to be more adventurous – if there are unfamiliar foods on the lists, set yourself a target to try one new ingredient a week. Really, though, deciding you are going to nurture yourself with a positive pantry and sticking to that plan, in whatever time frame works for you, is the most important part.

buying plant-based milks

If you are purchasing almond, coconut, soya, rice or hemp milks, make sure they are unsweetened and without additives (or as few as possible). Read that label.

The wonderful thing about grains is that they work as an excellent base for most meals. Even when your fridge and freezer are running low, if you have a kitchen stocked with grains, there will always be something you can cook and turn into a nutritious meal. With a little recipe inspiration, they can also be used as delicious snacks and the basis of different breakfasts too. I always have a variety of grains stocked in labelled jars, and I keep a close eye on how much I have so they don't run out.

Wheat-free and gluten-free foods are trendy; there's no doubt about that. However, behind the hype and the marketing around these foods, there are very sensible and significant nutritional reasons to broaden your grain horizons. Refined wheat grain, which is used in the vast majority of carbohydrates, is often heavily processed. Plus it is often used in foods that are packed with hidden sugars, chemicals and additives, and lacking in any real nutritional value. Indeed, some scientists are linking the reliance upon processed grains in our contemporary diets to increased incidences of Type 2 diabetes, heart disease, obesity and other serious conditions. Wheat also ranks high on the glycaemic index (for more on this see page 104), making it less than ideal if you're seeking sustained energy.

Unless you have an intolerance, I am not saying you have to eliminate wheat and gluten from your diet completely. However I recommend a gradual process of ridding your diet of as much as you can, learning how to cook with more nutritious options and making those swaps as often as possible.

There is a wide variety of 'good grains' that you can stock your pantry and fill your plate with that will make up for any void. Please don't be intimidated by their exotic names and provenance; they are all simple to cook, will give you plenty of energy and wholesome nutrition for a busy day, and, in eating them, you will be adding protein, vitamins and minerals to every serving.

||||||||||||||||||||||||||||||||||||||||||||||||||||||||||||||||||||||||||||||||||||||||||||||||||||||||||||||||||||||||||||||||||

WHOLE GRAINS Vs REFINED GRAINS

Whether you decide to go for wheat-free and gluten-free grains or not, there is one particular choice that you can make that will benefit your health: switching from refined grains to whole grains. As with sugar, it is always worth steering well clear of anything 'refined', and whole grains add greater nutritional value to your diet. This is because whole grains are made up of three components: bran, which forms the outer layer of the seed; endosperm, which is the kernel and bulk of the seed; and germ, which produces the sprout.

Those that have been refined (or 'processed') only contain the endosperm, and in the removal of the bran and germ they have also lost up to 80 per cent of their nutrients, which include iron and vitamins. Wholegrain foods also contain around three to six times more fibre than refined cereals or white bread, making them a much better choice all round.

||||||||||||||||||||||||||||||||||||||||||||||||||||||||||||||||||||||||||||||||||||||||||||||||||||||||||||||||||||||||||||||||||

wild rice

amaranth

black rice

barley

millet

polenta

black quinoa

freekeh

raw buckwheat/
toasted buckwheat

bulgur wheat

short grain
brown rice

quinoa flakes

khorasan wheat
(Kamut)

AMARANTH (GF) is high in iron, magnesium, calcium, protein and vitamin C. Along with buckwheat and quinoa, it is a 'pseudo-grain', which are in fact seeds but are so called because they have a similar nutritional profile to grains, as well as tasting and looking like them. As well as being gluten-free, amaranth provides two of the essential amino acids our bodies need – lysine and methionine. Amaranth has a subtle nutty flavour and looks a bit like couscous – small golden balls that become fluffy when cooked.

BARLEY is full of healthy minerals such as iron, magnesium, potassium and manganese, and, among other benefits, is thought to reduce blood pressure and lower bad cholesterol. Of all the wholegrains available, barley is highest in fibre. When cooked, it has a soft, chewy texture and can be used instead of rice in risotto or added to vegetable stews to make them wholesome and hearty.

When the bran has been removed and the grain is polished or 'pearled', this grain is known as 'pearl barley'. In this processing stage, pearl barley loses nutrients, which means it is not as good a choice as having the whole grain.

BLACK RICE (GF) is naturally gluten-free, richer in minerals and vitamins than brown and white rice, and has a nutty/earthy flavour. It is delicious used in both savoury and sweet dishes – I often substitute it for the brown rice in my Brown rice coconut porridge (see page 156). Buy it online or in Asian supermarkets. Soaking it for several hours helps to reduce the cooking time, which can be around 30-40 minutes.

BROWN RICE is a healthier choice than white rice, thanks to the high-fibre outer bran coating and because it has not lost any of its nutrients during the refining process. However, as a result, it takes a bit longer to cook than white rice and needs more water – cooking times are indicated on the packet.

You can get two different types of rice: short grain and long grain. Short grain is soft and sticky when cooked – varieties of short-grain rice are used to make risotto and sushi; long grain, which contains less starch, is drier and is therefore better suited to pilaus or dishes that will have sauce over the top.

||||||||||||||||||||||||||||||||||||||||||||||||||||||||||||||||||||

• raw buckwheat vs toasted buckwheat groats

You can buy two types of buckwheat groats, and it is important to know the difference — especially when working from a recipe.

RAW BUCKWHEAT GROATS are a cream colour with a slightly green tint. The groats have a lot of starch so they are soft and chewy and have a very mild flavour. To harden them, you can toast them in a dry frying pan over a medium heat for a few minutes, stirring until brown. They work well in porridge, home-made snack bars, soups and stews or sprouted for raw salads. Raw buckwheat takes between 8 and 30 minutes to cook, depending on the brand so check the packet.

TOASTED BUCKWHEAT GROATS, also known as 'kasha' or 'buckwheat kasha', are darker in colour (more brown/red). Their flavour is much stronger — slightly smoked and more bitter. These taste delicious in burritos or in veggie burgers. Toasted buckwheat usually takes slightly less time to cook but check the packet.

||||||||||||||||||||||||||||||||||||||||||||||||||||||||||||||||||||

There is a wide variety of 'good grains'. Don't be intimidated by their exotic names; they are all simple to cook and will give you lots of energy.

||||||||||||||||||||||||||||||||||||||||||||||||||||||||||||||||||

• bulk up with bulgur

Add some delicious texture and 'oomph' to any vegetable stew or soup by adding around 200g of raw bulgur wheat to your pan after you have sautéed your onions, garlic and vegetables. Then add your vegetable stock and cook as normal.

||||||||||||||||||||||||||||||||||||||||||||||||||||||||||||||||||

BUCKWHEAT (GF), in spite of its name, is not related to wheat. It is, perhaps surprisingly, a relation of the rhubarb family and is in fact a seed and another 'pseudo-grain'. It is gluten-free, packed with nutrients such as magnesium, potassium, zinc, copper, manganese and iron, and makes an excellent alternative to rice. I like to use it as the base of my salads (see page 183 for my Buckwheat tabbouleh).

BULGUR WHEAT contains iron, magnesium, potassium and manganese and is a good source of dietary fibre. Made from cracked wheat that has been par-boiled and dried, bulgur is golden in colour and, when cooked, the small grains are quite crunchy. You can use it in the same way as barley or quinoa.

FREEKEH is made from unripe green wheat that has been parched and roasted in order to burn off the husks. The result is a grain with a smoky flavour that can be used in all kinds of dishes ranging from salads to breakfast cereal to a delicious, hearty soup. It is not gluten-free, but it is more protein-, vitamin- and nutrient-rich than wheat. Freekeh is also high in fibre and low in carbohydrates.

KHORASAN WHEAT (KAMUT) is an ancient long brown grain which looks very similar to brown rice. It belongs to the wheat family and is sometimes referred to as 'Pharaoh grain' or by its main trademarked brand 'Kamut'. It is higher in magnesium, zinc and protein in comparison with 'modern' wheat. It is also a good source of dietary fibre. Kamut has a buttery, nutty flavour when cooked; it is sweet and without any bitterness. It can be used as the base of a salad, mixed with roasted veggies, chickpeas, wilted greens, cheese and tofu.

MILLET (GF) is a tiny yellow grain that is generally hulled when purchased from shops. It is gluten-free and is a good choice for heart health and also helps repair body tissue. The texture of the cooked grain is light and fluffy. To get the most from your millet, soak the grains with three to four times the amount of water for around six hours.

To cook millet, simply place the grain and water in a large pan with ½ teaspoon of salt and cook on a medium heat, stirring occasionally. For a creamier, porridge-like texture, cook your millet a bit longer (20 minutes). If you are using it to make veggie burgers or as a side dish, cut the cooking time down to 15 minutes to retain a crunchier consistency.

Goodness doesn't have to be bland or boring – here are a few easy ideas to add flavour, flavour and more flavour to your healthy grain staples.

serves 4, as a side

330g short grain
  brown rice
710ml water
½ tsp salt
2 tbsp miso paste
  (white or brown)

MISO BROWN RICE

In a medium-sized saucepan with a tight-fitting lid, combine the brown rice, water, salt and miso paste and bring it all to a boil. Stir a few times until the miso is dissolved, then cover and reduce the heat to low.

Simmer for 40–45 minutes (don't be tempted to lift the lid or stir). Remove from the heat and let it stand covered for 5 minutes. Then fluff with a fork and serve however you like. It tastes delicious with a large serving of greens.

serves 2, as a side

470ml water
200g white quinoa
½ vegetable stock
  cube
1 tsp cumin
½ tsp ground turmeric
¼ tsp cayenne pepper
  (or slightly less if
  you're not a huge
  spice lover)
pinch of ground black
  pepper
pinch of salt (optional)

SPICED QUINOA

In a medium-sized saucepan, pour in the water and bring to a boil. Pour in the quinoa and add the vegetable stock cube, cumin, turmeric and cayenne pepper. Season mildly with ground black pepper. Stir thoroughly, then pop a lid on the pan and leave for 30 minutes or until all the water has been absorbed.

Take off the heat, leave to cool slightly and then fluff with a fork. If you still feel it needs more seasoning, add a pinch of salt – although don't forget that this will already be in the dish thanks to the vegetable stock cube. You can then mix in lots of tasty extras to your quinoa, including wilted spinach, cooked beans or chopped avocado, or you can serve it as a side dish with roasted vegetables.

POLENTA (GF) is a great replacement for the typical carbohydrates of pasta, potatoes and rice because of its rich, starchy and comforting qualities. It is a golden-yellow gluten-free grain made from ground corn. Containing vitamins A and C, as well as iron and sodium, it is a great option to include in your menu. It is easy to prepare, filling and diverse in how it can be used: it can work as porridge for breakfast, as a base for any pasta sauce, with veggies in a soup, as a replacement for mashed potatoes or even cooked into a polenta cake for dessert.

||||||||||||||||||||||||||||||||||||||||||||||||||||||||||

• polenta and eggs

Polenta tastes great with eggs. Try topping your cooked polenta with poached eggs, wilted spinach and Parmesan cheese, or with a fried egg and steamed asparagus.

||||||||||||||||||||||||||||||||||||||||||||||||||||||||||

QUINOA (GF), the last of the three 'pseudo-grains', contains all nine of the essential amino acids, making it a complete protein. These tiny bead-shaped seeds have a firm texture, slightly nutty flavour and are gluten-free. They make an excellent alternative to couscous or white rice, and I love them as a protein injection at breakfast – see my Sweet quinoa and coconut morning pud on page 161. There are different types of quinoa available – white or ivory being the most common. There is also red quinoa, which is great for cold salads and holds its shape slightly better than white when cooked, as well as black quinoa, which is slightly sweeter and earthier than white. Mixing the varieties together creates a wonderful rainbow salad.

Quinoa is an absolute staple in my kitchen and gets cooked at least once a week and always as part of my prep day.

There are so many ways to use it (for lots of ideas see opposite), and it's quick and easy to whip up large batches that can be stored in the fridge for the week ahead.

||||||||||||||||||||||||||||||||||||||||||||||||||||||||||

• cooking quinoa

Once cooked, quinoa tends to hold water and can sometimes look a little soggy in the pan. A brilliant top tip, though, is when you have finished cooking, drain off any excess water and then put the quinoa back in the hot pan, though not on the hob, and replace the lid for 10 minutes. You will find any excess water or stickiness evaporates. Then just fluff it up with a fork for added lightness and texture.

• how to toast quinoa . . . and make it even better

Toasting quinoa before you cook it adds tons of extra flavour. Simply cover the base of a large sauté pan with a layer of quinoa and 1 tablespoon of coconut oil, then mix with your hands to ensure all the quinoa is coated in the oil. Pop it on the heat at a medium temperature and let it toast lightly for 10 minutes – stirring it all the time. If you want to cook it straight away, add your water to the pan you've used for toasting. It will be ready in about 20 minutes and you've only used one pan so there's less washing up too.

||||||||||||||||||||||||||||||||||||||||||||||||||||||||||

QUINOA FLAKES (GF) are made from the kernel being steamrolled into flakes. The flakes have the same health benefits as quinoa but are much quicker to cook and have an oat-like texture, making them best suited to making quinoa porridges.

eight simple ways to use more quinoa

Given how often I find myself cooking quinoa each week, I felt it was worth singling out this versatile seed for extra attention. It has multiple uses and is very easy to make in bulk and then eat throughout the week. There is a multitude of ways to get more quinoa into your meals.

Here are some of my favourite ideas for cooked quinoa:

01 Serve it warm for a sweet breakfast by adding toasted walnuts, grated apple, some raisins, a drizzle of maple syrup and nut milk.

02 For a savoury breakfast, top it with a fried or poached egg, some grated cheese and some cooked broccoli and mushrooms (freshly made or left over from the previous night), with a sprinkling of black pepper.

03 Add to your vegetable soups for a heartier, richer consistency.

04 Use it to stuff tortillas and make burritos – it goes wonderfully with black beans, grated cheese, chopped avocado and sliced tomatoes.

05 Try using it instead of rice or couscous for an added boost of protein.

06 Cooled, it is a great gluten-free base for a salad. There are many ways of making it extra delicious, but things you could consider adding are chopped cucumbers, cherry tomatoes, chickpeas, kidney beans, palm hearts, feta or goats' cheese, pine nuts, pomegranate seeds, dried apricots, rocket, olives, raw broccoli, cooked shredded carrots or courgette ribbons. When made as a large batch and kept in the fridge, these salads make wonderful packed lunches throughout the week.

07 Make guacamole (see page 245) and stir some cooked quinoa through to add delicious flavour and texture.

08 Stir a little into the mixture for black bean burgers (see page 208).

ROLLED OATS are created when whole oat groats have been steamed, then rolled into flakes. They can sometimes be referred to as oatmeal. If the oat flakes are rolled thinner or steamed for longer, they become known as quick or instant oats. Rolled oats are a source of protein, dietary fibre and antioxidants, and they contain iron, calcium, magnesium and potassium. They also contain absolutely no cholesterol, making them good for your heart. Jumbo oats offer a larger, thicker variety. Also rolled, they work well as a thicker porridge and are a great base for muesli and granola (see page 168 for my Low-sugar granola). I prefer using the gluten-free varieties, as you will see in my recipes, simply because it doesn't change the flavour at all and when I can make an easy swap like that to eliminate as much gluten as possible from my diet I do.

STEEL-CUT OATS are made from the same whole oat groats used for rolled oats but, instead of being processed and rolled, the groat is chopped into pieces by a steel mill. They are sometimes referred to as Irish oats or Scottish oats. They are slightly more chewy and nuttier in flavour than regular oats. They are a good source of iron, calcium and protein. Soaking the oats overnight dramatically reduces their cooking time.

TEFF (GF) is native to Ethiopia. It is a gluten-free member of the grass family and is a tiny grain – very similar to the size of a poppy seed, although slightly elongated in shape. This makes it ideal when you need a grain that will cook quickly. Teff has a high calcium content, and because it is high in resistant starch (which helps to promote the growth of 'good' bacteria in the colon), teff is considered ideal for colon health and blood-sugar management.

WILD RICE (GF), despite its name, is not actually a rice – it is a semi-aquatic grass, which means it is also gluten-free. It is hard to grow and therefore commands a higher price tag than other grains, so sometimes you will find it mixed with white and brown rice. Compared with white rice, it contains 30 times more antioxidants. It has not been refined and is high in minerals, essential vitamins and fibre. When cooked alone, it can take up to an hour to cook but, as a nutritious grain, it is worth buying and cooking it whenever possible. To cook wild rice, you just need to remember the ratio of 1 part uncooked wild rice to 3 parts liquid (i.e. water or vegetable broth). You will know when it has cooked because the rice will burst open when it's ready.

|||||||||||||||||||||||||||||||||||||||||||||||||||||||||||||||||||

• food safety with rice

Rice can be a food poisoning culprit so you need to observe a few rules when cooking and eating it. Rice should be served as soon as it is cooked, or cooled within one hour and put in the fridge if being eaten at a later time. If left at room temperature for more than two hours, it should be discarded; if stored in the fridge, it should be kept for no longer than one day. Rice should only ever be reheated once and it needs to be steaming hot.

|||||||||||||||||||||||||||||||||||||||||||||||||||||||||||||||||||

Grains each have different properties, which means their cooking times vary. It is good to familiarise yourself with this so that you know which grains are best for busy days and which are better for when you have more time.

There is also the matter of soaking. For some, this is familiar ground, however others will have never heard of this before. Essentially, although grains, legumes, nuts and seeds can be cooked and eaten without being soaked beforehand, soaking has a positive impact on their nutritional qualities and is thought to make them easier to digest.

Soaking comes under the topic of food science and can be a huge topic for discussion in itself. However, in simple terms, all edible grains, legumes, nuts and seeds contain, in varying quantities, something known as phytic acid – an anti-nutrient that prevents your body from absorbing minerals properly – and enzyme inhibitors, which can react badly with our digestive systems. By soaking them you can reduce or neutralise the phytic acid and enzymes, therefore improving the grain's nutritional quality and the body's ability to absorb its goodness.

So how do you best do this? When soaking grains, I just put the grain I need in a bowl and cover it thoroughly with warm water. It is important also to add an acidic ingredient in order to trigger the culturing/fermenting process, which neutralises the phytic acid; I use 1 teaspoon of lemon juice or raw apple cider vinegar to every 240ml of water. Because of the varying levels of phytic acid, each grain needs a different soaking time, although generally each needs to be left overnight and this is what I do.

With nuts and seeds, the amount of phytic acid they contain is much lower but soaking them in plain water will neutralise their enzyme inhibitors and also activates their benefical enzymes and increases their nutritional content.

To be honest, I don't always have time for soaking grains – so please don't feel you have to do it either – but I've made a pact with myself to try to do it as often as possible. I do, however, generally soak nuts; they come to life and become plump, moist and more flavoursome. I highly recommend giving it a try.

When I'm stuck for what to make for a meal, my go-to option is to take a grain as a base, then pull whatever I have in my pantry and fridge (chopped vegetables, beans, cheese, nuts and seeds) and mix it all together in a salad. To dress it, I use extra virgin olive oil or a flavoured oil, such as a nut or avocado oil, with apple cider vinegar, lemon and salt and pepper. You could also add lean meat or fish if you're not vegetarian.

If you are opting to follow a gluten-free diet – or even if you just want to reduce how much gluten you are eating – then another area that needs consideration, aside from the grains you are eating, is the types of flour you are using. These are most commonly used in baking, although they are used in some main course dishes too, and are often lesser-recognised sources of gluten. There are lots of good options available though that you can use instead of wheat flour. It may seem slightly daunting at first, given that these flours are not exactly the same as wheat flour in terms of flavour, texture, consistency and cooking times, but this section should help you to understand how you can use these substitutes in innovative ways.

ALMOND FLOUR makes a wonderful gluten-free alternative to wheat flour, and adds a deliciously sweet, nutty flavour to baking. Varieties include blanched almond flour (soft, lighter) and ground almonds (coarser, creamier). It is packed with goodness including protein, healthy fats, calcium, fibre, iron and vitamin E.

When using almond flour in place of wheat flour, simply substitute it like-for-like according to the recipe's requirements. Anything baked with almond flour will need slightly longer to sit once it has left the oven due to it being more delicate than anything cooked with wheat flour. See my recipe for a sugar-free tart made with almond pastry on page 233.

BUCKWHEAT FLOUR (also known as sarrasin flour) is a naturally gluten-free alternative to wheat flour. It is fine and soft in texture, and has a strong flavour that is slightly nutty. It is a grey-ish brown colour.

Although it has a wide range of uses, it can't be used as a like-for-like substitute for wheat flour as it has different properties and therefore reacts and cooks differently. I use it to make sweet and savoury pancakes (see pages 163–4 and photo opposite);

they are deliciously thick and fluffy and slightly different to traditional ones, but this means they are easier to hold and eat on the move, making them great after-school snacks for my children.

COCONUT FLOUR is produced by drying coconut meat at a low temperature once it has been pressed for its milk. It is then ground into a soft, fine powder. Coconut flour is gluten-free, protein- and fibre-rich, a good source of healthy fats and great to use in baking. It has very different properties from grain flour though so cannot be directly substituted. Coconut flour absorbs a lot of liquid so you need a lot less of it than traditional wheat flours.

QUINOA FLOUR is produced from unprocessed raw quinoa seeds. It is light and fluffy and gluten-free. As quinoa contains protein it's wonderful to be able to make breads that have both protein and fibre. It has more of a nutty flavour than wheat flour and pairs well with fruits, nuts and warm spices like cinnamon and nutmeg. It works best when baking bread, pancakes, waffles and cakes, and for thickening stews and sauces.

Nuts play a very important role in a healthy plant-based lifestyle and are a staple in my family's day-to-day diet. Firstly, these little nutritional powerhouses all contain protein, good fats, vitamins and minerals. Secondly, a handful fills you up, gives you energy and satisfies hunger. Lastly, they are super easy to transport as snacks and they are simple to add into a variety of recipes. Remember, it's important to eat them in their natural, pure state to reap the benefits – don't reach for nuts coated in sugar, artificial flavours and oils.

ALMONDS (*whole and sliced*) are really handy to have in your cupboard given how extensively they can be used. They contain a number of nutrients, including vitamin E, calcium, iron and magnesium, which are good for keeping bones healthy, your immune system strong and your hair and nails glowing. Almonds are usually eaten raw but are great toasted when added to salads, casseroles and desserts.

ALMOND BUTTER is made by blending almonds into a crunchy or smooth paste (see page 80 for my recipe to make your own). The word 'butter' is slightly misleading as it is dairy-free. Although susceptible to oil separation, generally all almond butter requires is a good stir before it's ready to use. Always look for nut butters without palm oil and sugar. Just nuts on the ingredients list is what you want.

ALMOND MILK (*unsweetened*) is a great swap from dairy; it has a very rich, sweet flavour and is naturally low in fat. Almond milk is also a good source of vitamins A, C, D and E and a rich source of calcium; it also contains iron and magnesium, making it an all-round great choice. When buying store-bought almond milk, check the ingredients list to ensure it is unsweetened or, better still, make your own.

It's so much easier than you might expect to make your own nut milk. It guarantees you have a pure milk, without any fillers or preservatives, and it's a fun project to do with your kids.

Soak 465g of almonds in water overnight.

The next day, drain the water, rinse the nuts and place them in a high-powered blender with 710ml fresh cold water. Blitz together until the nuts are pulverised.

Pour the mixture through a mesh strainer covered in a muslin or tea towel (or use a proper nut-milk bag) into a bowl to remove the grit from the nut pulp.

Push the purée through with a spatula to ensure none of the milk is lost, or squeeze the bag well, and then finish by adding a little water if you prefer a thinner consistency. The milk will stay fresh in the fridge for up to 5 days if kept tightly sealed.

You can add flavours to almond milk when blitzing, including a teaspoon of cinnamon, ginger, star anise, nutmeg, liquorice root powder or cardamom. Or you could try adding superfood powders such as spirulina, chlorella, blue-green algae and/or maca.

CASHEWS come from the bottom of a fruit called the cashew apple, making them officially 'seeds'. As such, some people with nut allergies are able to tolerate them. Cashews have zero cholesterol and are rich in minerals such as magnesium and copper, which are thought to benefit bone strength and improve cognitive ability. They can be used as the base of home-made nut butters. See below for how to make your own.

• make a change from dairy: cashew cream

Dairy isn't the only way to enjoy a cream. There is also a very simple way of using cashew nuts to make soups, sauces and dips creamy and rich – all without a drop of dairy and with the added benefit of plant power.

1. Take 310g of cashews (to make about 710–950ml of cream), cover with water and leave to soak overnight or for as many hours as possible.

2. The next day, drain and rinse the nuts, then pop them into a high-powered blender or food processor, and cover the nuts with 2.5cm of water. The more water you include, the less thick and creamy it will be.

3. Add 1 tablespoon of lemon juice for added kick, then whizz it all together. It will be done when it's completely smooth.

4. Stir this cashew cream into absolutely any soup you're making at the end – it will be rich and delicious.

PEANUTS (raw and unsalted) actually belong to the legume family – they aren't a nut – but of course we all think of them as such and they have lots of the same properties so I've listed them here. Rich in monounsaturated fats, peanuts are considered good for the heart, and are also good sources of vitamin E, protein and antioxidants.

PEANUT BUTTER is a popular paste that is generally made from ground dry-roasted peanuts, although there are lots of variations available. Try to look on the ingredients labels for brands with no sugar, added salt or palm oil – or, better still, make your own from scratch (see below).

how to: make your own nut butter

It's easy to make your own nut butter. You can use almonds, cashews, hazelnuts or peanuts according to what you prefer.

Simply put 420g of soaked nuts (with their skins on) and 1 tablespoon of soft coconut oil into a food processor and blitz until the nuts become finely ground. Then blitz again until they turn into a paste. Transfer to a jar or sealed container and store in the fridge. Nut butters are delicious spread on rye bread, added to smoothies, served with healthy desserts, or smothered on chopped apple or in the centre of celery as a snack.

WALNUTS are considered by some nutritionists to be the king of all nuts because they are high in good fats, protein, antioxidants and vitamin E. They are also high in omega-3 fatty acids (which are beneficial fats our bodies need to function at their best); a handful provides over 100 per cent of your daily recommended amount. I love adding them to breakfast staples like porridge, muffins, granolas and mueslis, but they are equally easy to sprinkle into salads, add to cookies or just eat plain on the go.

Although understandable given the name, thinking the coconut is a nut is a mistake. The coconut is actually a fruit: a drupe, or stone fruit, like cherries, plums and peaches. I'm a huge fan of these tropical imports because they taste absolutely decadent, provide a lot of flavour and are a healthy substitute for other oils or butter. There is such a wide variety of uses for coconut and you can buy and use it in so many different forms, so it is one of my key pantry essentials – and I want it to become one of yours too.

To begin, there are two different types of coconut: those that are brown and have a hairy husk, and those that are green and smooth. They're both the same thing, except the former is the older or 'mature' version; the green ones are young coconuts. Although we're more familiar with the brown variety, in the tropics – where these fruits come from – it is typically the green coconuts that are used.

Brown coconuts have a lot more meat than the green and the meat is thicker, firmer and white. It is full of flavour and often eaten raw or used in cooking. The meat of green coconuts is soft and gelatinous with a weak flavour. However, the mature coconuts have very little 'water' inside them. In comparison, the younger coconut is full of the clear coconut liquid, which is filled with electrolytes. This is the liquid you'll be drinking if you buy 'coconut water'.

Coconuts are sold in so many different forms that it's often a minefield to know what you're buying, how to use each product and when. Here's my guide to navigating the wonderful world of the coconut.

COCONUT BUTTER is made from the meat of a mature coconut. It is puréed into a creamy butter. You can either use it straight from the jar (like almond or peanut butter) as a spread, use it as you would butter in cooking or add it to smoothies or soups to make them rich and creamier.

COCONUT CREAM is found in cans or can be bought as dried, hard blocks and diluted with hot water before use. It has a higher percentage of coconut fat than coconut milk, making it thicker and creamier. It is a liquid that needs stirring before use to avoid separation. You can use it in home-made curry recipes, as an extra to help make your smoothies super creamy or in any puréed soups.

COCONUT FLAKES (*unsweetened*) are similar to desiccated coconut, in that they are made by drying coconut flesh to remove the moisture and then shredding it, but the flakes are larger. Make sure you're buying the flakes without added sugar as many brands do add sugar to sweeten them. You can sprinkle coconut flakes on top of leaf or quinoa salads, curries and soups, add them to your muesli or granola, mix them into a Chia seed pudding (see page 171) for added crunch, or sprinkle them on top of Vegan ice cream (see page 237).

coconut milk
(from a carton)

coconut milk
(from a can)

coconut cream

coconut water

desiccated
coconut

coconut oil

fresh coconut

COCONUT MILK is made from the grated flesh of a brown coconut, rather than the liquid found inside the nut. The process that goes into making coconut milk is also the same for producing coconut cream.

You can buy two types of coconut milk: cans of milk, which you'll find in the canned food aisle and milk in a carton, which is in the refrigerator aisle, often among the dairy milks. Despite sharing a name, the two are very different ingredients. Canned coconut milk is thick and creamy, although not as thick as coconut cream (see page 81). It is used in cooking for curries, sauces and desserts. Coconut milk in a carton is not as rich in flavour, is often watered down and is a thinner liquid. It is intended more for drinking – and used like you would a dairy milk, to be added to smoothies and poured over granola or porridge.

||||||||||||||||||||||||||||||||||||||||||||||||||||||||||||||||||

• coconut snacks
Toasting coconut flakes is great for enhancing the fruit's rich nutty flavour and creating a delicious snack. Simply place the desired amount of coconut flakes in a large frying pan and cook over a medium heat, stirring often. When the flakes are mostly golden brown, they are ready. You can also add a variety of flavours, coating the flakes lightly with curry powder, cayenne pepper, cumin or turmeric for something savoury, or with cinnamon and nutmeg for a sweeter effect.

||||||||||||||||||||||||||||||||||||||||||||||||||||||||||||||||||

ten things to do with a can of coconut milk

1. Freeze it in an ice cube tray and add cubes to smoothies for an exotic, creamy twist.

2. Blend it with plenty of garlic, salt and spices and use it to marinade chicken.

3. Stir it into your puréed vegetable or bean soups to make them luxurious and rich.

4. Pour it over chopped fruit for an instantly delicious dairy-free dessert.

5. Pair it with sticky black rice and sliced mango for a traditional and healthy Asian dessert.

6. Soak grains in coconut milk overnight to infuse them with flavour.

7. Use it as a braising or poaching liquid for seafood, such as salmon or prawns.

8. Add flavour to hearty cooked greens such as kale by heating 180ml of coconut milk with 1 tablespoon of lemon juice and 2 tablespoons of extra virgin olive oil and drizzling it over the top.

9. Use it to make whipped cream to serve with desserts: chill the can overnight and whip the firm milk with an electric whisk.

10. Use it in your curry recipes for richness and a creamy texture (see my sweet potato, kale and chickpea coconut curry on page 205).

how to: make your own coconut milk

Switching from cow's milk to plant-based milk is a great way to add more plant-based foods into your diet. The cartons of coconut milk are a good option (though check the label to make sure there aren't any added sugars), but home-made is so delicious and I think it's fun to have a go at making your own.

Put 90g of unsweetened desiccated coconut into 710ml of boiling water and let it soak for around 10 minutes.

Pour the mixture into your blender and whizz it together until smooth.

Put your strainer over a bowl, line it with your muslin or tea towel and pour in your coconut milk.

Let it drip through, give the cloth a good – but gentle – squeeze to ensure no liquid is left (the pulp will still be in there and can be used for your baking) and then pop the milk into an airtight bottle in the fridge. It will keep in a tightly sealed container for up to 4 days. Shake well before use.

COCONUT OIL is a pantry staple that you won't want to run out of in a hurry. Not only is it full of nutritious benefits, it can also be used as a face and hair mask if you're in need of some body hydration too.

Coconut oil is made from the extracted fat (oil) of the coconut meat. It becomes hard in cold temperatures and many recipes call for softened coconut oil, so you can either heat it gently on a low temperature on the hob, put the required quantity in the microwave for 30 seconds

or pop the jar in a bowl of warm (not boiling) water and it will quickly melt. I always keep coconut oil in my cupboard instead of the fridge so it remains slightly soft and ready to use. On hot days you may find it's already liquid so just be careful when you open the jar.

It cooks at a high heat so works very well as a substitute for most oils in cooking. Use it as a replacement for vegetable oil when pan-frying, or brush it on veg before baking or roasting them in the oven.

Coconut oil is also great to use in raw sweet treats as a binding agent or as a dairy substitute for butter.

||||||||||||||||||||||||||||||||||||||||||||||||||||||||||||||||||||||||||

• top tip: buying coconut oil

When you look for coconut oil, make sure you opt for unrefined coconut oil. This is when it has been extracted directly from the coconut without any refinement, filtering or extras being added. Because it hasn't been altered or affected in any way, it has greater flavour and is richer in protein, vitamins and antioxidants. Refined coconut oil is almost void of protein.

||||||||||||||||||||||||||||||||||||||||||||||||||||||||||||||||||||||||||

COCONUT WATER is the clear liquid found in the centre of a young green coconut. It can be drunk directly from the fruit or bought packaged. The consistency is very different to coconut milk so it shouldn't be used as a substitute. Naturally low in sugar (it contains approximately a fifth the amount of sugar other fruit juices do), coconut water helps remedy dehydration by providing the body with electrolytes, such as potassium and sodium, which are important for the heart and digestive and muscle health. Drink it fresh and use it in your smoothies (see page 177).

This category is essential to a balanced plant-based lifestyle because all these little wonders are complex carbohydrates, providing vitamins, minerals, antioxidants and protein with every bite. They are considered 'heart-healthy' foods because of their high fibre content and they all digest slowly, giving you more lasting energy and keeping you full for longer.

ADZUKI BEANS are small, red beans with a sweet, nutty flavour. Simply boiled, they are a delicious accompaniment to brown or black rice. I often add them to my chilli (see page 187), and they blend well with vegetables in dips (see page 245). They are a good source of magnesium, potassium, iron and B vitamins, and contain lots of fibre and protein.

BLACK BEANS are rich beans that are as tasty in soups, stews and dips as they are in cold salads, burgers and even brownies (see page 228); versatile is their middle name. I always reach for them when time is short to serve them simply with a bit of olive oil, salt and pepper or to add to other dishes for a fibre and protein boost.

CANNELLINI BEANS are white and creamy and full of antioxidants. I like to use them for bulking out veggie stews; simply adding them to red onion sweated in olive oil with a dash of lemon juice as a side portion for a larger meal; or cooking them with rosemary leaves, olive oil and chopped garlic then mashing them to make a thick, delicious topping for bruschetta.

CHICKPEAS are loaded with protein, fibre, iron, vitamin B6 and magnesium. Just 2–3 tablespoons of the golden balls equates to one of your daily recommended five portions of fruit and veg. I love them for their rich texture and versatile flavour, which makes it easy to mix them with other veggies and spices. They blend smoothly into rich dips, can be roasted to make snacks (see page 219) or just added to salads, soups, curries (see page 205 and photo opposite), stews and pasta sauces.

LENTILS come from the pea family, and are rich in iron, B vitamins and calcium. There are several varieties and which you choose depends on what you are cooking: firm green and brown lentils are best for salads, while red and yellow split lentils are best for soups and stews because they soften quickly and easily and have a smooth texture, which blends into the background. They're a staple in my house because I find them so easy to use (see page 44). They're tasty hot or cold, and mix well with so many spices, herbs and other vegetables.

RED KIDNEY BEANS have a high fibre content, meaning they stop blood sugar levels from spiking too rapidly after a meal. Kidney beans can be used as a burrito filling, cooked with other beans to make a colourful bean salad or mixed in with soups, stews and chillis (see page 187).

SOYA BEANS are bright, young green beans that come in pods and need to be shelled. They have a firm yet smooth texture and are a good source of protein. Popular in Asian cooking, the beans are often boiled or steamed in their pods, tossed with salt and served as 'edamame'.

seeds

They may be small, but seeds are nutritional powerhouses. Most have a mild flavour, meaning they can quite easily be mixed into a dish, adding wonderful health benefits and texture. In the case of pumpkin and sunflower seeds, a handful also makes a delicious snack.

CHIA SEEDS are tiny grey, white or black balls. Packed into their small form is a powerful combination of nutrients, including fibre, healthy fats and calcium. They are a particularly valuable addition to a plant-based diet because they are a very rich source of protein and amino acids (for more about these and their importance to our diet, see page 26). Not only do chia seeds contain the nine essential amino acids we need to obtain from our food but in fact they contain a total of 18 of the 22 amino acids. They are also full of antioxidants and are naturally gluten-free.

FLAXSEEDS (also called linseeds) are small brown seeds packed with a wealth of omega-3 fatty acids. You can get your recommended daily intake of these healthy fats in 2 tablespoons of flaxseeds. The seeds can be bought whole, ground, as a powder or as an oil, but to reap the nutritional benefits it's best to buy ground – or grind them yourself – as whole flaxseeds may pass through your system without being digested. Sprinkle 2 tablespoons of ground flaxseeds into your muesli, granola or over yoghurt and chopped fruit; add them to smoothies or pancake batter; or make my Low-sugar granola (page 168) and Matcha cacao macaroons (see page 222).

HEMP SEEDS are another rich source of good fats and protein. They also contain all nine essential amino acids so they are a powerful addition to a plant-based diet. You can buy hemp seeds in a variety of ways: shelled, roasted, cracked or ground. When cooking, I find the best variety to use is shelled; if you need a smoother consistency you can grind up the shelled hemp seeds yourself in a food processor. I sprinkle them over salads, mix them with pancake and savoury muffin batter, and add them to porridge, muesli and smoothies. Hemp seeds can also be pressed into oil – it has a smooth, nutty flavour.

PUMPKIN SEEDS are flat oval-shaped dark green seeds that come in a white-yellow shell. They are generally eaten hulled and are chewy with a soft crunch. They have a nutty, slightly bitter taste and are a valuable source of zinc, iron, magnesium, copper and potassium. They also contain vitamin E, and offer a diverse combination of antioxidants. Pumpkin seeds can be eaten alone or mixed in with cooking. I like to include them in my granola recipe (see page 168) and often sprinkle them over my salads.

Chia seeds are great to add to smoothies for a burst of protein and nutrients but they absorb a lot of liquid so use a touch more liquid than your recipe suggests.

SESAME SEEDS are jam-packed with minerals including copper (which is known to help in reducing the pain and swelling for those suffering from rheumatoid arthritis), calcium, magnesium, iron, zinc, vitamin B1 and dietary fibre. They have a subtle nutty flavour and come in a variety of colours including white, black, yellow and red. They're great for mixing into stir-fries, and I also like sprinkling them over steamed veggies with some lemon juice. When I eat chopped apple with a nut-butter dip, I often have a bowl of sesame seeds available to dip the apple in for extra crunch. Tahini is a paste made from ground, hulled sesame seeds. It can be eaten as a dip on its own, used in other dips or in salad dressings (see pages 247 and 249).

SUNFLOWER SEEDS are a wonderful source of nutrients, including magnesium and vitamin E. They are crunchy grey seeds that can be eaten plain or roasted, or added to granola, porridge and muesli. They are also delicious ground into a paste to spread on bread or crackers and can be used as a nut substitute in many recipes. In fact, for anybody with a nut allergy, sunflower seeds are the best alternative in a recipe that calls for nuts.

power supplements

Adding a supplement like the ones below to your food and drink can be a valuable way of boosting the nutrients in your diet, as well as bringing new flavours to your cooking. They're often referred to as 'superfood' powders or supplements, mainly because a huge amount of minerals, vitamins and amino acids are packed into a very small quantity. Whether you add a teaspoon to your smoothies, sprinkle them over your salads or mix them into your pancake batter, these powders are a versatile and wonderful addition to any wholefood, plant-based diet. They're available from most good health-food shops so do give one or all of these a try; they are potent sources of goodness.

AÇAI POWDER comes from the grape-like berries of the açai palms. The fruits are high in fibre, calcium, vitamin A and monounsaturated fat; they also contain iron This goodness is all retained in the powder, and the flavour is delicious too. It is often described as being like a cross between a juicy blackberry or raspberry and a chunk of dark chocolate – it's both rich and bitter at the same time. It can be added to a number of foods, such as smoothies or yoghurt, and sprinkled on top of muesli or porridge. Around 10–15g per 200ml serving is recommended.

BAOBAB POWDER comes from the African fruit which is rich in vitamin C, calcium (it contains more than twice the calcium level of cow's milk) and potassium. It is almost 50 per cent fibre. With one of the highest antioxidant capacities of any fruit in the world, expect baobab to become an increasingly well-known household name. All you need is a teaspoon or two and you can sprinkle it over your porridge or muesli, mix it into pancakes or healthy snack bars, stir into smoothies or salad dressings, or mix it with coconut water to drink.

BARLEYGRASS POWDER comes from the barley plant and is rich in minerals including magnesium, calcium and zinc. It is also rich in protein and vitamin E, and has more than a third of your recommended daily intake of iron in a single serving. Around 2–3 teaspoons is enough for a serving, and you can use it in a variety of ways. Try mixing it in with salads, soups, smoothies and sauces.

BEE POLLEN contains nearly all nutrients required by humans, making it an excellent ingredient to include where possible. It can be expensive – which is hardly surprising given that it takes one bee an entire month of working eight hours a day just to produce 1 teaspoon – but you don't need to use a lot each time; just a teaspoon or two goes a long way. It is approximately 40 per cent protein, so is actually more protein-rich than any animal source and, weight-for-weight, contains more amino acids than eggs, cheese or beef.

CHLORELLA is a type of green algae. It is absolutely loaded with vitamin B12 – a 5g serving (about 1 teaspoon) contains 880 per cent of your recommended daily intake – and is one of the best non-animal sources. It is good for detoxifying and cleansing your body and is thought to help fight disease. It also contains vitamins A, B9, C, E and K, along with minerals including calcium, iron, magnesium and potassium. Add to smoothies or juices.

LUCUMA is another antioxidant-rich fruit that, ground into a powder, works well as a natural and nutrient-dense sweetener. It is high in B vitamins, carbohydrates, fibre and minerals such as calcium and phosphorus. For a vegetarian, this is a wonderful addition to your meals as it contains a substantial concentration of iron, which in turn, leads to increased energy levels. Due to its sweet flavour, it is best mixed in with smoothies, sweet sauces, or healthy home-made desserts. It is recommended to use around 2–3 teaspoons per day.

MACA is a Peruvian root that is part of the radish family. It is ground into a powder and makes a wonderful energy supplement, although when you first start using it you should begin with small amounts (about 1 teaspoon) and progress to a larger quantity (1 tablespoon). This is because, while you cannot overdose on maca since it's a food, people have reported having nervous energy and increased heart rate from taking too much; it is always advisable to work your way up and to allow your body to adjust slowly. It works best mixed into smoothies and drinks.

MATCHA is made by grinding green tea leaves into a fine powder. Originating from Asia, it is loaded with goodness; its benefits range from improving concentration and boosting energy to detoxifying the body naturally. Just one cup of matcha tea contains 137 times more antioxidants than a regular green tea, and it has the same as 10 cups in terms of nutrients. It is a great source of fibre, chlorophyll, vitamin C, zinc and magnesium, among other benefits. You can enjoy matcha as a cup of tea or mixed into recipes such as my Matcha cacao macaroons (see page 222) or Frozen matcha cheesecake (see page 234).

MORINGA POWDER is made from the dried leaves of the moringa tree, which is widely referred to as 'the miracle tree' in parts of the world due to how many benefits and nutrients it contains. Moringa powder is a rich source of plant protein

and contains iron, magnesium, calcium and vitamins A and E. It works as an anti-inflammatory, detoxing the body and getting rid of any excess acids. It tastes fairly similar to green tea and complements a sweet green smoothie well.

PLANT-BASED PROTEIN POWDERS

come in many variations, including hemp, rice, chia and pea protein. Eating a plant-based protein powder is a great way of supercharging your diet, especially if you work out a lot and want to keep on top of your protein intake or are vegan or vegetarian. Hemp is a particularly important one, because it is a complete protein, meaning it contains all nine essential amino acids. Serving portions vary but are usually clearly stated on packaging. I use protein powders mixed into smoothies, Bircher mueslis, overnight oats, muffins and sometimes even bars and cookies.

Spirulina is a blue-green powder that comes from natural algae. Rich in chlorophyll, it is loaded with B vitamins, antioxidants and essential amino acids, among other nutrients. It is particularly good for vegetarians and pregnant women as it has a naturally high iron content and is also high in protein and magnesium. It has quite a strong flavour so it is best to start with 1 teaspoon per day initially, and gradually build up to a tablespoon according to your taste. It can be mixed into lots of other flavours so is great in smoothies. I also like to mix it into sweet treats, such as my Coconut spirulina energy balls (see page 224).

|||||||||||||||||||||||||||||||||||||||||||||||||||||||||||||||||||||||||||||||

• top tip: supercharge your honey

Mix 3 tablespoons of Manuka honey with ¼ teaspoon of spirulina and ¼ teaspoon of cinnamon for a drizzle of sweetness bursting with goodness. Store in a sterilised glass jar or air-tight container and use in the same way as you would normal honey.

|||||||||||||||||||||||||||||||||||||||||||||||||||||||||||||||||||||||||||||||

WHEATGRASS is thought to be gluten-free, although it comes from the young shoots of the wheat plant. It is at this point that the grass is at its most fertile and nutritionally-rich time. As well as being high in calcium, it also contains vitamin E, zinc and copper. Like barleygrass, a single serving contains over a third of your daily recommended iron intake, making this a bountiful source for vegetarians. Around 2–3 teaspoons is enough.

healthy snacks for kids

Edamame, the pop-able little soya beans make great snacks — hot or cold. Simply boil the pods in water for 3–5 minutes or steam them for 5–10 minutes. Leave to cool a little, then pop the beans out and lightly sprinkle with Himalayan or sea salt. I also use them as a counting tool with my kids to help them with their maths homework. If they really want something sweet, instead of a chocolate bar, a fun idea for a treat is to put a banana on a stick, spread some honey on it and roll it in carob powder and chopped almonds.

While many of my staples may be familiar to you, below are some of my favourite ingredients for adding punch and extra flavour to the things I cook; I hope you'll give them a try.

APPLE CIDER VINEGAR is a popular choice as a store-cupboard vinegar, thanks to the numerous ways it is thought to benefit health. It is rich in potassium and enzymes, which help with fatigue. I love to use it in salad dressings, with seaweed, in marinades and to give dips a tangy kick.

||||||||||||||||||||||||||||||||||||||||||||||||||||||||||||||||

• top tip: cleaning vegetables

As well as using apple cider vinegar in your cooking, it can be used as a great natural way to clean your vegetables if you haven't bought organic, due to its antimicrobial properties. Simply create a solution of 10 per cent vinegar to 90 per cent water in your sink or a large bowl and briefly dip your vegetables in it, move them around and then rinse them thoroughly. Avoid doing this for anything with a fragile skin, as they will either be damaged or soak up too much vinegar in the process.

||||||||||||||||||||||||||||||||||||||||||||||||||||||||||||||||

BALSAMIC VINEGAR is sweet and sour. It originates from Italy and starts off as the juice of just-harvested white grapes before being boiled down, fermented and concentrated. As well as being a delicious choice for salad dressing, it can also be drizzled over the top of food – although a little really does go a long way.

EXTRA VIRGIN OLIVE OIL is full of healthy fats and antioxidants, and is made by crushing olives and then extracting the juice. Of all the cooking oils available, extra virgin olive oil (and extra virgin coconut oil) is the only one made without chemicals or industrial refinement.

MISO PASTE is a fermented paste made from soya beans and either rice, wheat, barley or rye. The most common variety is light yellow/brown in colour and it has a mild, salty flavour. The darker kinds – more red/dark brown in colour – have a stronger, even saltier flavour. There is also sweet white miso (also known as shiro), which is a pale yellow colour and has a creamy texture, a sweeter flavour and has been fermented for a shorter period of time. I like to use it to make dressings, to marinate tofu or tempeh, or to brush on vegetable kebabs.

MUSTARD (English, Dijon, wholegrain or any that you find you like) is always handy to keep on stand-by. Mustard-plant seeds are loaded with anti-inflammatory compounds, essential minerals such as selenium, plus antioxidants. The less processed the mustard, the better, and you should always keep an eye out to check if any nasty extras have been added. Mustard is delicious as part of salad dressings, added to sauces for extra flavour or used as a spicy dip.

SESAME OIL is a fragrant and slightly sweet vegetable oil often used in Asian cooking. You can buy two varieties: plain, which is the milder of the two and well suited to both cooking and table use, and toasted, which is much darker in colour and has a strong, nutty flavour. I use sesame oil in dressings (see page 248), in dips (see page 242) or simply drizzle it over steamed vegetables or Brown rice bowls (see page 211) to add Asian flavour.

TAMARI is a type of Japanese soy sauce made from fermented soya beans. Unlike soy sauce, which includes wheat, tamari has little or no wheat – check the packaging as it's usually made clear on the front label. Rich in flavour, thick in texture and not as salty as traditional soy sauce, tamari is often used to create marinades and salad dressings (see my Tamari baked tofu on page 211 and my Tastiest tamari dressing on page 248).

||||||||||||||||||||||||||||||||||||||||||||||||||||||||||||||||||||||

• top tip: condiments for your little ones

As a parent I decided early on that I wasn't going to offer my children ketchup with everything, which is a habit many fall into. Instead I opened their palate to mustards (not the super spicy kinds though) from a young age and I now offer it to them instead of ketchup whenever we have chicken strips or potatoes. It has become a firm favourite.

||||||||||||||||||||||||||||||||||||||||||||||||||||||||||||||||||||||

other bits and pieces

There are a few extra ingredients that I always keep in the pantry because they add tons of flavour but they don't fall into any of the categories I have discussed so far.

CACAO POWDER is made by pressing then grinding raw cocoa beans. It is the purest type of chocolate available and the process keeps all its living enzymes and removes the fat. It is a more nutritious choice than cocoa powder as it has not undergone the same processing, does not have any dairy added and contains less sugar. To read more about cacao, see page 120.

CAPERS technically belong in the plants chapter – they're flower buds – but you can buy preserved capers in jars to keep in your pantry. They add a slightly sour, salty flavour to savoury dishes and are generally preserved in brine, olive oil, wine vinegar or salt.

CAROB POWDER makes a fabulous dairy- and caffeine-free substitute for chocolate. It is great in smoothies and baked goods. It comes from the roasted and ground pods of the evergreen carob tree, and contains less fat than cocoa. It is not without natural sugars, so should still be seen as a treat, but it is definitely healthier than chocolate.

DRIED SEAWEED is available to buy in different forms. Dulse is a red seaweed that looks a lot like shredded cabbage and has a delicious smoked flavour that makes it a great accompaniment to meat or vegetables. Wakame is a very commonly eaten seaweed and has a subtle sweet flavour. It is delicious in soups and salads; you will often find it in miso soup. It is green in colour and looks more like the seaweed we're used to seeing along the British coastlines.

These seaweeds are quick to prepare: just soak them in water for 5 minutes – they don't need any cooking. My favourite

way to eat them is to mix different types together with my Great green tahini sauce or No-sugar peanut sauce (see page 247).

There are lots of other varieties to try. Popular kinds include nori, which comes in thin green sheets and is often used as the outer layer for sushi wraps. Kombu, which comes in long, thick black strips, has a mushroom-type flavour. It is used largely when making soup stock and is then discarded, although it can be cooked with rice, grains and beans or prepared as a side dish. Another type is arame, which is a sea oak used commonly in Japanese cooking. It has a sweet, slightly delicate flavour and makes delicious salads. It is a good place to start if you're not used to eating seaweed.

GOJI BERRIES are from the same family as potato, tomato, chilli pepper, aubergine and tobacco. They have been used in Chinese medicine for over 6,000 years and are now widely considered a 'superfood' as they are thought to boost the immune system and brain activity. They are rich in vitamins C, B2 and A. When making your porridge or muesli for breakfast, why not sprinkle over some goji berries?

MARINATED ARTICHOKES are really wonderful when bought fresh from a deli, but they are also great to buy marinated in glass jars to keep in the pantry. A good source of vitamins and minerals, they taste delicious mixed in with salads or pasta dishes.

NUTRITIONAL YEAST is a deactivated yeast that comes in the form of dry yellow flakes, which you sprinkle over, rather than slice or stir into dishes. As its name implies, it's packed with great nutrients – it contains all nine essential amino acids, making it a complete protein, as well as lots of vitamin B12, folic acid and zinc. As well as its goodness, I love it for its fantastic flavour –it tastes like cheese – and I sprinkle it over salads, pasta dishes, popcorn, soups, steamed veggies, rice dishes and omelettes. Once you start to use it, I guarantee it will become a household staple for you too.

OLIVES *(green and black)* have numerous health benefits, helping to control blood pressure and eliminate excess cholesterol from the blood. They are also thought to enhance fertility, protect against anaemia and protect cells against cancer. They are great sources of vitamin E, dietary fibre and amino acids. Olives make a delicious snack eaten whole and add a lovely Mediterranean twist to salads and pasta dishes.

PALM HEARTS are a vegetable harvested from the inside of palm trees. They are similar to artichokes in texture and flavour and come in cans. They look a bit like large white asparagus but without the tips, and their natural flavour is quite woody and subtle. They are low in calories, while high in fibre, iron, magnesium and vitamin C. They are also a source of zinc, calcium and potassium. I love to munch on them plain straight from the can (so do my kids) but they are equally delicious added to lettuce- and grain-based salads.

SUN-DRIED TOMATOES are either sold dried or soaked in olive oil to preserve them. They can be scattered on top of bruschetta and bring a sweet and intense flavour to any dish, including pasta sauces, egg dishes, salads and vegetable soups.

04

sugar:

where it hides and how to ditch it

t here are really only two things you need to know about sugar. Firstly, that we eat far too much of it; secondly, that sugar is not your friend, let alone the benign, comforting substance that food companies – and cultural conditioning – would have you believe. Sadly sugar isn't just an innocent teaspoon of sweetness here or there, but one of the nation's unhealthiest addictions. In the past decades, sugar has gone from an occasional treat to a daily 'necessity', hidden in everything from ketchup to granola. And it is having a correlative, hugely negative toxic effect on our health, weight, teeth and well-being.

But fear not! The nation's addiction to sugar is something I'm on a mission to cure, one lifestyle at a time. I'm here to help you understand why sugar is so detrimental to your health, where sugar hides and how you can truly kick the habit for good.

our sugar plan

By the end of this chapter, I hope you will be fully versed on what sugar is, the effects it has on us, where it hides and how we can reduce its influence on our lives. Of course the ideal is to cut sugar out completely, but I'm a realist so the advice I always give is to reduce your sugar consumption as much as you possibly can. No matter how much you consume, less is better than no change at all. The more you reduce, the more positive results you will see. The key is to make better choices surrounding sugar and, where possible, to either avoid it, reduce your consumption or use better substitutions.

so what exactly is sugar?

This might seem like an obvious question to begin with – in fact, so obvious that there is likely to be some temptation to skip this section. But actually, it's not quite so simple and, in part, that is precisely the reason why we eat so much of the stuff without ever noticing it.

The white or brown sugar that you add to your tea or find on kitchen tables is sucrose. This is harvested and refined from sugar beets and sugar cane. But that is just one variety of 'sugar'; in fact, any ingredient that ends in '-ose' also denotes a variety of sugar – glucose, fructose, dextrose, maltose, lactose and high-fructose corn syrup are just a few examples.

To make it a little easier for you, given how many names there are for added sugars and sweeteners, I have drawn up a full list for you on page 102. All these substances are known as 'added sugars' when included in our food products and have absolutely no nutritional value. They're just a bunch of empty calories and nothing else. Meanwhile, artificial sweeteners and substitutes may be calorie-free but they also stimulate insulin production. It is well worth taking a photo of this list or ripping it out and keeping it in your bag so that when you go shopping and check ingredients labels, you can remember what to look out for. There is no question that these terms serve to disguise sugar and deliberately bamboozle consumers, turning food into a sugar minefield.

read the label

Here is a list of all the words used on food labels that indicate a type of sugar or sweetener has been included. As I explain on page 106, some are better choices than others – and even those should be used sparingly.

- acesulfame potassium
  (or acesulfame-k)
- agave nectar *(or syrup)*
- artichoke syrup
- aspartame
- aspartame-acesulfame salt
- barley malt syrup
- blackstrap molasses
- brown rice syrup
  (or rice malt syrup)
- cane crystals
- cane juice crystals
- cane juice solids
- cane sugar
- caramel
- carob syrup
- coconut palm sugar
- coconut sugar
- corn sweetener
- corn syrup
  (or corn syrup solids)
- date sugar
- demerara sugar
- dextran
- dextrin
- dextrose
- diastase
- erythritol
- ethyl maltol
- evaporated cane juice
- fructose

- fruit juice
- fruit juice concentrate
- fruit juice crystals
- galactose
- glucose
- glucose solids
- glycerin
- glycerol
- golden syrup
- grape sugar
- high-fructose corn syrup
- honey
- hydrogenated starch
- hydrolysate inulin
- isomalt
- lactitol
- lactose
- luo han guo
  (or monk fruit)
- malt syrup
- maltitol
- maltodextrin
- maltose
- mannitol
- maple syrup
- molasses
- naturlose
- neotame
- oligofructose
- palm sugar
- panela

- panocha
- rapadura
- raw honey
- raw sugar
- reb a
- rebiana
- refiner's syrup
- rice syrup
- saccharin
- sodium cyclamate
- sorbitol
- sorghum syrup
- stevia
- sucanat
- sucralose
- sucrose
- sugar alcohols
- sugar beet
- sugar cane
- sweet sorghum
- syrup
- tagatose
- treacle
- trehalose
- turbinado sugar
- xylitol
- xylose
- yacon syrup
- yellow sugar

No, not exactly. Sugar isn't just a case of filling our bodies with empty calories and absolutely no nutrients – it is also highly addictive. When we eat it, we are sent on a roller coaster, which leaves us craving the 'highs' whenever we hit the 'lows'. It is a vicious cycle that becomes very difficult to break free from.

Now for the science – how does this work biologically? To put it in simple terms, sugar is a simple carbohydrate (meaning it is made of one or two molecules). When we eat foods containing these simple carbohydrates (such as refined sugar, honey, maple syrup, fruit juice, etc.), the body quickly digests them and rapidly turns the simple carbohydrates into glucose (energy) in the bloodstream.

Because this happens in a short space of time, it causes our blood glucose levels to rise very sharply. This creates the 'highs' of the roller coaster. As there is too much glucose in the bloodstream, the pancreas releases insulin to help process and regulate the glucose levels, speeding up the rate at which it is absorbed into the cells in the body. This causes blood sugar levels to decrease, creating the 'lows'. So, if we eat foods that trigger a slower, more stable reaction from the body, it creates a more gentle, consistent response.

During the crash, or 'low' – when there is a rapid change in our blood sugar levels – we can be left feeling fatigued, shaky, drained of energy and craving more sugar. It's not all that different from the way drug addiction works, as scary as that sounds. And it's not just chocolate bars and sweets that cause this reaction in us either; starchy foods such as crisps, white bread, pasta and chips work in a similar way. Although these are complex carbohydrates (containing three or more sugar molecules), making them slightly different to sugar, they lack the fibre and vitamins of other complex carbohydrates such as wholegrains (see page 64), vegetables and legumes, and the body breaks them down into simple sugars quickly so they can still make your blood sugar surge and crash in a similar way to sugar.

The good thing about sugar addiction, however, is that it is a cycle that can be broken. You can train your taste buds to prefer foods that are less sweet.

the health implications

If anything can convince you to go sugar-free it has to be understanding the impact that the white stuff has on your health. It is the reason I am so bothered about it and the reason we should care. The sad reality is that our health has become severely impacted as a result of people's excessive sugar consumption with expanding waistlines, increased blood pressure, a heightened risk of obesity, and diseases such as Type 2 diabetes and heart disease all on the rise. There are now almost two billion overweight adults worldwide and, as a 2012 NHS report found, more than a quarter of all adults in England are obese. This rate has risen threefold since 1980. There is no question about it: sugar doesn't just give you a sugar 'high' or make your kids hyper – it is systematically changing the face of our society's health and well-being. If we don't start taking charge of our health now, goodness knows what the future will have in store for the next generations.

sneaky sugar

Common sense tells us we probably shouldn't be eating lots of cakes, sweets and biscuits for a healthy lifestyle, but what's more difficult is cutting out the foods we don't know are packed with sugar. Even if you have cut out foods such as sweets and fizzy drinks, there is still a high chance you are eating far more sugar than you realise.

Manufacturers are very sneaky. They know we are addicted to sugar, so they know that the more they put into their foods, the more we will crave them and the more we will buy.

According to the NHS, the average person in Britain consumes 140 teaspoons of sugar each week. That's over a 500g bag of sugar – or more than 24 chocolate bars.

However, as I mentioned, the types of sugar found in the foods that we eat are incredibly diverse and don't always fall under the word 'sugar' on the label. It means that we, as consumers, need to be far more clued up about the answer to 'What is sugar?' in order to be able to rid ourselves of it and truly feel the benefits.

To really eliminate sugar from our diets we need to look far beyond the ordinary sources and learn how to read manufacturers' food labels. Sugar is prominent in a huge amount of what we eat, even in places that you would not naturally think to look for it – for example, sauces, marinades, yoghurts and bread (see page 106 for a fuller list).

Then there are the seemingly healthier choices, which are still laden with added sugar. 'Healthy' cereals and cereal bars quite often have a very high sugar content. Research undertaken by Action on Sugar in 2015 found that many children's breakfast cereals contain as much as 3 teaspoons of sugar per serving. To give you an idea of what this is in real terms, it would be like putting two-and-a-half chocolate biscuits on their plate each morning. Not many parents would feel good about doing that and yet we have convinced ourselves that processed foods like muffins, cereals and breakfast bars are a healthy alternative.

GI who?

When you hear a food described in terms of its GI (glycaemic index), this is a measure of how it affects your blood glucose levels. If it has a high score — typical of sugar, white bread, white pasta, white rice, etc. — then it is absorbed very quickly into your bloodstream and triggers the roller coaster effect described on page 103. If it has a low score, then it is absorbed more slowly and helps maintain a much more steady blood-glucose level, which helps to prevent sudden energy dips, mood swings and waves of fatigue.

# of sugar looks like this....

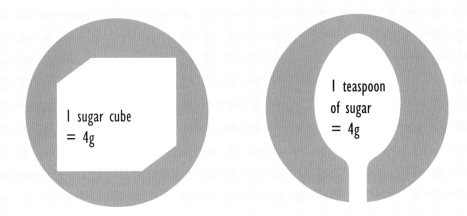

I sugar cube = 4g

I teaspoon of sugar = 4g

Fruit juice and squash, which are so often pitched to parents as an important element in their children's diet, are laden with sugar. The same goes for tomato ketchup, fruit yoghurts, canned vegetable soups, deli meats, sports drinks and so forth – and yet these aren't things that people immediately associate as being bad for them.

how much sugar do we actually consume?

According to the NHS, the average person in Britain consumes roughly 140 teaspoons of sugar a week. Picture that in your mind. That equates to just over 15 cans of Coca-Cola (which each contain 9 teaspoons of sugar) or just under 24 milk chocolate bars (which contain on average 6 teaspoons of sugar each). It's a lot of sugar, and that is just the average, so there are also many people who are eating more than that.

But what exactly are the recommended amounts? How much of the sweet stuff is too much? Experts have said that our bodies are only designed to handle half that quantity, and ideally a lot less, per week. The NHS and World Health Organization both recommend that added sugars – and by this I mean anything that has been added to the food, rather than anything naturally occurring, such as fructose in fruit and lactose in milk – should make up no more than 5 per cent of the amount of energy (otherwise known as 'calorie intake') that you get from food and drink per day. In measurements, this equates to around 30g (7.5 teaspoons) of sugar for adults per day. This is all variable, however, depending on your size, your age and how much you move.

When you start cutting out sugar from your diet, you will be met by a number of alternatives that will present themselves as being healthier options. The sugar substitute market has been growing year-on-year, and some substitutes are better than others but overall they are all sweeteners and should be used minimally and as a treat. Here is the low-down on the ones you will notice most as you begin your sugar overhaul.

AGAVE NECTAR (OR AGAVE SYRUP) comes from the agave plant, which is better known for being used in the production of tequila. It has a somewhat similar texture and taste to honey, and is commonly advocated in 'healthier' cooking. Agave syrup falls low on the glycaemic index, however, because it is around 90 per cent fructose (depending on the brand) – ranking the highest of any commercial sweetener, aside from pure liquid fructose – so it is not the best choice to make. The one benefit is that as agave syrup is one-and-a-half times sweeter than sugar, you can afford to use less but it should still be used sparingly.

COCONUT SUGAR is becoming a popular alternative to sugar. It is made from the sugary sap of the coconut palm. This sap is collected and then placed under heat until the majority of the water has evaporated. What is left is the sugar, which looks like a cross between brown sugar and bee pollen. It is not the same as palm sugar, which, although similar, comes from a different type of palm tree. Coconut sugar retains a fair amount of the nutrients found in the coconut palm, including minerals such as calcium, potassium, iron and zinc. However, it is very high in calories and, in order for you to really see the benefits of the nutrients it contains, you would have to use a sizeable amount. It makes a good, but not great, choice.

RAW HONEY is, of course, made by bees, which collect nectar. Nectar is a sugar-rich liquid found in plants, and bees turn this into the honey. Not all honey sold is raw, however; some has been pasteurised, which means it has lost a lot of its nutritional value during this processing. It is therefore important to always check what type you are buying. Like agave syrup, honey is very high in fructose. In fact, by weight it is about 82 per cent sugar, with 40 per cent of that being fructose, so you should only use it sparingly. The microorganisms that it contains also mean it is not suitable for young children, especially those under the age of one, because their bodies cannot handle it in the same way as adults.

MAPLE SYRUP is made from the sap of the maple tree. The sap is collected and then boiled until most of the water evaporates. This leaves a thick syrup, which undergoes filtering to extract any impurities. It comes in numerous grades, which can be identified by the colour. Grade A covers three groups: light amber, medium amber and dark amber. The darkest shade of maple syrup is Grade B. Grade B is no healthier than Grade A but it has a stronger maple flavour and is better for cooking. It is important when buying maple syrup to look for the pure kind. There are many cheaper versions that are maple-flavoured and these will be full of refined sugars or high-fructose corn syrup. Even though maple syrup is a fair choice of sweetener, and one I use in my recipes, it should still be used sparingly. It is a treat – not something to use regularly.

STEVIA is a plant-based sugar substitute extracted from the stevia plant, which is grown naturally in Brazil and Paraguay. It can taste 200 times sweeter than table sugar thanks to naturally occurring glycosides (a type of molecule, to put it simply) but contains no calories or carbohydrates. Some people think it has a very distinctive taste, which you either like or don't, but overall I think it's a good choice.

XYLITOL has perhaps the most unnatural sounding name of all the sugar substitutes, yet it is actually a substance found naturally in the fibres of many vegetables and fruits – and it is predominantly extracted for commercial use from corn cobs. However, it is extracted using a process called 'chemical hydrogenation', leading many to claim it is misleading to call it 'natural'. It has a low GI value, absorbs slowly into the body and is thought to prevent the growth of bacteria in the mouth, meaning it can improve dental health too.

||||||||||||||||||||||||||||||||||||||||||||||||||||||||||||||||||||||||||||||||||||||||||||||||||||||||||||||||||||||

TWENTY-ONE
surprising foods
that contain a
lot of sugar

|||||||||||||||||||||||||||||||||||||||||||

- Barbecue sauce
- Canned or packaged fruit (*there are naturally occurring sugars in fresh fruit*)
- Cereal
- Coleslaw
- Dried fruit
- Energy/protein/'healthy' snack bars
- Fat-free foods
- Flavoured waters
- Flavoured yoghurt
- Fruit drinks
- Fruit jams
- Granola
- Instant porridge
- 'Jazzy' coffees, such as blended or 'frappe' lattes, flavoured coffees
- Milkshakes
- Pasta sauce
- Processed breads
- Ready-made soups
- Ready-made vinaigrettes
- Salad dressings
- Sports drinks

fruit, glorious fruit?

One of the better-known vehicles for 'naturally occurring sugar' is fruit. It is quite commonly brought into the sugar debate, and yet what confuses people the most is that it is widely touted as being good for us. It's all a bit baffling, right? After all, doesn't an apple a day keep the doctor away?

Well, while fruit is not fundamentally bad for us, the amount we eat can be detrimental. Many nutritionists recommend that adults and children eat only two pieces of fruit per day, and ideally those containing lower quantities of fructose, such as apricots, berries, clementines, grapefruit, nectarines, peaches and plums. Fruits higher in fructose – such as cherries, dates, figs, pears and watermelons– should be eaten less frequently.

||||||||||||||||||||||||||||||||||||||||||||||||||||||||||||||||||||||||||||||||||||||||||||||||||||||||||||||||||||||||

THE JUICE ON FRUIT

But when it comes to fruit juice, none of that matters – it's all bad! When fruit is juiced, any positives are literally squeezed out of it. This is why fruit juice is often referred to as 'sugar water' by many nutritionists. Natural, whole fruit has relatively little sugar, when compared to a fizzy drink, for example, which has a massive amount, but when you juice fruit and concentrate it, then it has nearly as much sugar as the fizzy drink. If you want to think about it in terms of quantity, a 330ml can of Coca-Cola contains 35g of sugar while here are some fruit comparisons:

- A GLASS OF GRAPE JUICE HAS: 38G OF SUGAR
- A GLASS OF CRANBERRY JUICE HAS: 37G
- A GLASS OF APPLE JUICE HAS: 28G
- A 500ML VITAMINWATER: ESSENTIAL HAS: 27G
- AN AVERAGE GLASS OF FRESH ORANGE JUICE HAS: 21G

It is an undeniable truth that we shouldn't be starting our mornings or hydrating our kids with fruit juice. And the sooner we realise this, the better it is for our health and well-being. There is an exception to the juice rule and a way to drink juice in abundance – and that is green vegetable juice. So, in a nutshell, go green veg or go water!

Home-made smoothies are also slightly different. Because you are blending the fruit, not juicing it, you are keeping much of the fibre and therefore they are a good contribution to your two-piece per day allowance. Moderation is still important though, especially as blending fruit can make it seem like you are consuming less than if you were eating it whole and although they are technically a drink, their texture and content means that smoothies are more of a meal or snack than a source of hydration.

||||||||||||||||||||||||||||||||||||||||||||||||||||||||||||||||||||||||||||||||||||||||||||||||||||||||||||||||||||||||

FRUIT YOGHURTS: THE TRUTH ABOUT WHAT'S ON YOUR SPOON

Did you know that fruit yoghurts are notoriously misleading in how good they are for you? Children love them, generally because they are so sweet and colourful. However, they're full of added sugar – often between 4 and 5 teaspoons' worth. So what can you eat instead?

- Buy full-fat yoghurt. Not only does it taste better, but you will find low-fat varieties are also full of sugar to make up for what has been lost in flavour when the fat is removed. Always opt for plain or natural yoghurt that is made from whole milk and live cultures. Then add real fresh fruit on top yourself. Anything with fruit flavourings or 'real fruit' will mean it has concentrated or added sugar.

- Because it is dairy, buy organic where possible, but don't view 'organic' as meaning it is therefore sugar-free or good for you. It is still important to read the ingredients label. Quite often, organic brands will have added sugar or flavourings, but they will just be organic sugar. What buying organic yoghurts does mean is that the milk used is free from antibiotics, pesticides, herbicides, fertilisers and hormones.

- Try plain coconut yoghurt made out of coconut milk and flesh as an alternative. However, please note: this is not coconut-flavoured yoghurt, which is dairy with added sugar and coconut flavourings.

alcohol and sugar

When it comes to alcohol, it's pretty clear that it is lacking in nutritional value. However, what might not be quite so well known is that many alcoholic beverages are also full of sugar. When the grapes are ripening to produce wine, they contain fructose and glucose (in roughly equal amounts); these are important for the fermentation process. Then, as the alcohol levels are increased, the sugar levels drop. The producer can control how much these levels drop though, and this is how they make wine either dry or sweet. To put this into context, a dry wine – whether red or white – contains around 1–2g of carbohydrates (sugars) per 200ml glass. However, a sweet wine can contain over 10g of carbohydrates for the same amount. A wine of medium sweetness will have 5–10g of carbohydrates in a 200ml glass. Fortified wines are even sweeter: a glass of port can contain up to 20g.

Meanwhile, studies have found that a pint of cider contains as many as 5 teaspoons of sugar, while a glass of gin and tonic can contain around 3½ teaspoons. And the NHS claims that drinking 5 pints of lager a week over the course of a year is equivalent to eating 221 doughnuts!

I'm not saying you should abstain from alcohol forever, but cutting back is always a good idea. And if you are going to drink spirits, they should be served with healthier, low-sugar mixers like soda water or coconut water, rather than lemonade, full-sugar fizzy drinks or juices. Try also to be mindful of what you are eating while you are drinking; often alcohol goes hand-in-hand with unhealthy snacks such as crisps or chocolate.

So what steps should you be taking to rid yourself of your sugar addiction and reduce the amount of sweet stuff in your life? I'm going to break this down into a week-by-week plan over one month. That is really all it should take timewise to rid yourself of cravings and sugar addiction; however, don't worry if it takes slightly longer. We may all be human beings but we are put together in very different ways, so what works for one person may not necessarily work for another in the same time.

As with everything I've been telling you throughout this book, the important thing is simply that you commit to making a start and that, ultimately, you just keep trying. If you feel you can make more than one change per week then by all means do so, but if that seems quite daunting, don't worry. As long as you are actually making changes, slowly but surely you will see progress. The key is that you make that first step to do this for you.

One thing I do want you to do throughout the whole month is keep a rough sugar diary of what you are eating. It will really help you track your progress and all the positive changes you are making. Simply write down what you have eaten for your breakfast, lunch, dinner and snacks – as well as any drinks you have had, alcohol or otherwise. This doesn't have to be scientific or precise – I'm not asking you to start weighing your food or measuring out your drinks first. If you have anything with a packet though, one really helpful thing to do is to make a note of what the sugar quantity is for the item and log that next to it. The aim overall is to have a rough but honest overview of all you have consumed in a week.

At the end of each week, it is a good idea to sit down and review everything you have written. Start by highlighting or marking out foods that were obvious sugary indulgences. Pop these in a list at the bottom as the first foods you will be trying to cut out.

Then, using the list on page 106 and your knowledge of how to read nutritional labels (see opposite), write a second list at the bottom of all the foods containing hidden sugars that you want to start avoiding.

If you want to take it a step further, you can also add up all the sugar quantities for each food to work out how much this equals in total throughout the whole week. You will then be able to compare this weekly total over the course of the month to see whether it stays the same or drops accordingly. Looking at the sugar levels will really help you track and monitor your progress.

As you begin to take on more steps to becoming sugar-free each week, make sure you also log all the positive changes you experience too, such as better concentration, less grumpiness, fewer mood swings, more energy and more consistent weight management. That way you can be proud of the improvements you are making to your life and well-being, simply by changing this one element – sugar. It's strong stuff, so ridding it from your life step by step can be revolutionary.

One thing you will hear me repeating throughout this book is that you need to 'read the label'. It sounds obvious, I know, but with the busy pace of our lives this is often sidelined and we instead take at face value the product name, the words on the front of the packaging or the marketing that surrounds the product.

So once you're looking at a nutrition label, how do you actually read the nutrition beyond just seeing a confusing list of words and numbers?

First, the label will tell you either what the numbers are measured against – this is often 'per 100g' –or it can also be 'per ½ can', 'per slice' or 'per serving'. It is worth taking into account that when you come to eat it, you may have more than 100g or half a can – serving suggestions often differ vastly from the amount we actually eat – and therefore the numbers would increase accordingly.

Below the nutritional information, you will find the list of ingredients. These will be in order from high to low of how heavily they feature within the food. If sugar features high on the list, put it down immediately. Do keep in mind that if the label says 'no added sugar' it does not necessarily mean it is free of sugar. If a product contains naturally occurring sugar, it won't be listed, and items such as yoghurts, milk and fruit juice all contain naturally occurring sugars.

When it comes to added sugar in solid food products, 5g or less per 100g is considered low, between 5g and 22.5g per 100g is considered medium, and more than 22.5g per 100g is considered high. Please note that, although some products now have a colour-coded traffic light system on the front to show whether they are high in certain values, even if sugars are showing as being green or amber, it is still important to read the labels on the back to work out how much sugar you will realistically be consuming by buying that product.

Begin to take the time to stroll the aisles of your local grocery store, unearthing sugar in all its stealthy guises.

stay mindful of marketing
Behavioural scientists believe that something called a 'health-halo effect' exists, in which we eat more of foods when they are marketed to us as being healthier, even if they actually aren't. Given how much 'healthy' has become a buzzword for this era, marketing will only ramp up its efforts in this respect, knowing full well that this is where consumers are turning their attention.

Making the change to becoming sugar-free can seem overwhelming to some, so in your second week start easing it out of your diet gradually by making some really easy sugar-free substitutions. Have a go at making at least one swap a day for the next seven days. If you are feeling confident, raise the bar to two changes per day.

Start your swaps at breakfast, because if you start your day with sugar, you are simply setting yourself up for a huge energy crash around midday and will likely be clambering to the shops for another fix. Next look at your lunches, your dinners, your snacks, your drinks and how you 'treat' yourself throughout the day.

Below are my suggestions for a few easy switches. As you will see, these are not just limited to obviously sugary foods; they apply to your entire diet. The goal of these swaps is to help you make healthier choices with everything you eat and drink. You may wonder how this relates to sugar . . . the answer is that if you stock up on the right foods in all areas of life, then you are less inclined to pick up sugary foods or make poor choices when hungry. In cutting out sugar, it really is about looking at what you eat overall, as well as the smaller things that add up to much bigger problems.

BREAKFAST SWAPS

- **Cereal with milk** ➜ chia seed pudding (see page 171) or overnight oats (see page 159)

- **White toast with fruit jam** or **Nutella** ➜ rye toast with a nut butter (see page 80 for how to make your own) or avocado on toast (see page 175)

- **Pancakes with sugar** or **syrup** ➜ gluten-free buckwheat pancakes (see page 163) with cashew cream (see page 80)

LUNCH SWAPS

- **Sandwiches made from white bread** ➜ rye bread or gluten-free bread sandwiches (though check for sugars and fillers) such as my TLAT (see page 194).

- **Ready-made soups** ➜ home-made, low-sugar vegetable soups, such as my spiced chickpea, brown rice and veggie soup (see page 193).

- **Salads with ready-made dressings** ➜ salads topped with extra virgin olive oil, apple cider vinegar and lemon, or any of my salad dressings (see pages 248–9).

nori

fresh coconut

tamari ginger
roasted chickpeas

zesty lemon
coconut almonds

kale chips

DINNER SWAPS

- **Takeaway curry** ➜ sweet potato, kale, chickpea and coconut curry (see page 205)
- **Meat with sugary marinades** ➜ healthy chicken fingers (see page 148)
- **White pasta with ready-made tomato-based pasta sauce** ➜ a gluten-free pasta with home-made tomato sauce (see page 202) or pesto (see page 241)

SNACKS SWAPS

- **Crisps** ➜ kale chips or my tamari ginger roasted chickpeas (see page 219 and opposite)
- **Chocolate bar** ➜ my low-sugar matcha cacao macaroons (see page 222) or sunshine sunflower balls (see page 220)
- **Snack bars** ➜ a handful of raw unsalted seeds and nuts or gluten-free oatcakes with chopped avocado or hummus
- **Dried fruit** ➜ fresh fruit or dried unsweetened coconut flakes

DRINKS SWAPS

- **Morning latte** with **milk** or **cream** ➜ matcha green tea
- **Concentrated cordial** or **squash** ➜ home-made or cold-pressed vegetable juice
- **Fruit juice** ➜ coconut water, iced herbal teas or water infused with lemon, cucumber and ginger

||||||||||||||||||||||||||||||||||||||||||||||||||||||||||||||||||||||||||||||||||||||||||||||||||||||||||||||||||||||||||||||||||

These may sound like a lot of changes, especially as the above covers every meal, but you really can do as many or as little of these as you feel comfortable with. Don't let yourself get stressed over it; remember, this is a marathon, not a sprint! Take things at your own pace. The key is making that first change, and then you will naturally find yourself building on this. If swapping foods feels daunting, perhaps just pick two or three per week to try. Or just focus on one meal first, then gradually start making changes to the rest of your meals.

By the end of this week, whether you have made one swap or 20, you will feel good about having made the effort.

If there is one thing I hear all the time when it comes to people cutting down on sugar, it is that they seriously struggle with their chocolate addiction. Now, there are two ways of dealing with chocolate addiction: either go cold turkey or gradually decrease how much you eat. So, for example, you could cut down by only having a few cubes rather than the whole bar, and then gravitating towards chocolate containing 70 per cent cocoa solids or more instead of milk chocolate. However, while dark chocolate is a better and healthier choice than milk chocolate, don't be fooled into thinking this means it is free from sugar. A small 35g bar of 70 per cent chocolate can contain around 30 per cent sugar. The buzzword here is 'moderation' – eating little and less frequently is key.

And while dark chocolate is a better and healthier choice than milk chocolate, don't be fooled into thinking this means it is free from sugar.

Another change worth considering is switching to cacao, which is the purest type of chocolate available. Raw cacao is produced when unroasted cacao beans are cold-pressed. The process helps to keep the living enzymes within the cacao bean and also removes the fat, which is known as cacao butter. The pressed bean can then either be eaten whole, roughly ground into chunks as cacao nibs or ground into a powder. Raw cacao is full of natural antioxidants that work to boost your health, it contains a lot less sugar than cocoa and is free from dairy, so is definitely a better choice than chocolate where possible.

Another switch to try is carob. Carob tastes earthy with a caramel, nutty flavour and the texture is slightly creamier than chocolate. It is made using the sweet edible pulp from within the pods that come from the carob tree. The pods look very similar to broad beans, albeit dark brown in colour, and the plant they are from is part of the pea family. The seeds contained within are inedible. However, the pulp can be dried, roasted and ground into a powder that looks very similar to cocoa. You can also get carob chips, which look similar to chocolate chips. Carob contains three times the amount of calcium as cocoa powder. It also contains half the amount of fat and is caffeine-free. However, it is not free from sugar entirely; therefore, while it is a better choice, it should still be enjoyed sparingly.

05

breakfast:

*wake up and smell
the real food*

breakfast is important, hugely important, so don't let anyone – especially yourself – tell you differently. Sadly though, in our bid to get out the door quicker, have that extra 10 minutes in bed or simply because we have convinced ourselves we don't need it, breakfast seems to be the meal that suffers most in our ultra-fast-paced lives. Yet it is the meal that is so easy to pack more plants into and sets us up, both physically and mentally, for the next 12 hours. It provides all the necessary fuel that we need to work and feel at our optimum.

This meal is about breaking an overnight fast of 8–12 hours (hopefully). While this has given your digestive system the vital time it needs to recover, now that you are awake, it is important that you give your body the best possible fuel to reboot and re-energise.

Also, on a psychological level, I believe having a healthy breakfast is a key to how well the rest of your day goes – both in terms of eating and in general too. If you make the commitment to having a nutritious breakfast, you will feel proud of yourself for starting your day well – for caring enough about yourself to make the effort – and you will naturally want to maintain that momentum throughout the day. I assure you that after a week of fuelling yourself on the right foods in the morning, you will feel far more equipped to tackle each day and make healthier choices throughout the week.

better breakfast: *keep it real*

You are worth good food! We need to educate ourselves so we can choose what constitutes a 'good' breakfast and eliminate what will leave us with an empty tank hours later, reaching for a sugar-laden energy boost. Together we can change bad, ingrained breakfast habits and create a new 'normal' breakfast in your kitchen – a breakfast consisting of real foods that energise your body for the day ahead, instead of putting it on a roller coaster of sugar highs and lows that affect your productivity and mood for the entire day. I want to make this as simple as possible so what follows are my five steps to a better breakfast.

breaking the fast
Most nutritionists recommend a break of 12 hours without food overnight, which means no late-night snacking. Try to have as early a dinner as your schedule allows and then leave the kitchen for the evening.

STEP ONE: BREAKFAST ISN'T DESSERT

Next time you are out shopping, here's a challenge for you. Pick up two or three cereals that you or your kids enjoy eating and read the label. Where does sugar come on the list? How many times is it mentioned in different guises? (Consult my list of all the ways sugar is hidden by different names on page 102.) When it comes to sugar, we must get into the habit of reading the nutritional information and deciding for ourselves what is a healthy choice. There are so many other foods that you can buy to avoid eating lots of sugar in the morning – and hopefully I will be inspiring you with these throughout this chapter.

STEP TWO: SIMPLE MORNING SWAPS

If switching from sweet pastries and cereals to savoury breakfasts seems slightly daunting, then why not try some smaller swaps to begin with? These are similar to what you may currently be eating, so will feel familiar, but are loaded with plants and are much better for you.

- If you love a bacon sandwich, make a fried-egg sandwich on healthy gluten-free or rye bread and fill it with lettuce, tomato, basil leaves and avocado in addition to the egg.

- Rather than buying sugar-laden granola, have a go at making my Low-sugar granola on page 168.

- If you're craving a full English breakfast, then make yourself an omelette with spinach, feta cheese and courgette, or Super scrambles (see page 172).

- If you love fruit-flavoured yoghurt, start buying plain full-fat yoghurt and pour in frozen blueberries or raspberries and mash them up a bit – they turn the whole pot pink and make it delicious but without the added sugar.

- Try swapping dairy milk for unsweetened nut, coconut, soy or rice milks (see pages 78 and 84 for how to make your own).

- Also refer to page 114 for extra breakfast swap suggestions.

These are all simple substitutions that will leave you feeling equally as full – if not more so – but won't cause you to have a crash in energy and motivation later in the day.

STEP THREE: OPEN YOUR MIND

Big food companies want you to think that breakfast needs to come out of a box or a package; it doesn't and it shouldn't! In changing and opening up your preconceived beliefs about what breakfast is, your options suddenly increase and improve.

Adding more savoury foods into your breakfast routine and using plants and nutritious grains as your inspiration, is a good place to start. How about scrambled eggs with chopped courgette, spring onion and green peas? Or maybe some Miso brown rice (see page 68) topped with a poached egg, or a wrap filled with hummus and shredded veggies? Sometimes I will have half an avocado with balsamic vinegar or roasted sweet potato wedges with a sprinkle of salt and pepper.

Be open-minded about what breakfast can mean. My dad eats greens with chickpeas and cayenne pepper most mornings, and I have a friend who loves to eat seaweed, tofu and miso soup first thing. My point is there is no wrong way to eat a plant-based breakfast and there's nothing that shouldn't be considered 'normal'.

STEP FOUR: PREP AHEAD

I don't know anyone who has lots of extra time in the mornings. Even if you don't have children and you're not racing around gathering homework, sports kits and packing lunches, you may be trying to fit in a gym session before work, get a jump-start on your commute or be simply running late. So prepping ahead is an essential way to ensure a healthy breakfast will fit into your day – and it takes just minutes of prep the night before. (That said, if you really don't have the time or inclination, turn to page 132 for my ideas for breakfasts you can fling together in the morning in no time at all.)

swap sugar for cream
Instead of automatically adding a sweetener like maple syrup, honey or agave syrup to your breakfast, try using a hearty drizzle of coconut cream instead — it's rich, creamy and naturally sweet.

prep ahead ideas

01 Chia seed pudding (see my recipes on page 171) is a great prepare-ahead choice as you can make it in minutes the night before, allowing the chia seeds the time they need to absorb liquid and swell. You can make a huge batch with minimal effort and then just pull it out whenever you need to throughout the week.

02 If you're planning on having scrambled eggs (see page 172) with greens, crack open all your eggs and whisk them in a bowl, wash and chop all your greens and leave both in the fridge overnight.

03 My low-sugar granola recipe on page 168 can be made at the weekend and used throughout the week.

04 Porridges (see pages 156, 160 and 161) are also great to prepare the night before; place your grains in a pan with water and/or a plant-based milk and leave to soak overnight with added extras like slivered almonds, blueberries, cinnamon and coconut flakes. They take far less time to cook this way.

05 Assemble your smoothie ingredients (see page 177–9), except the frozen ones, in a blender jug and pop it in your fridge (if it will fit), then the next morning add any frozen ingredients and whizz it up. It always tastes better if you blend it fresh in the morning.

06 Hard-boil a dozen eggs (see page 47) to pop on your children's plates during the week or for you to pop in a Tupperware box and eat at work or on the run. I usually pair them with sliced avocado, some leftover black beans and a piece of wholegrain or gluten-free toast.

Another great – and very easy – way of speeding things up in the morning is to try eating leftovers from dinner the night before as part of your morning meal (if you're not having them as lunch of course). Provided your evening meal was healthy (I'm not talking pizza here), there are lots of fabulous and creative ways to use it twice.

||||||||||||||||||||||||||||||||||||||||||||||||||||||||||||||||||||||||||||||||||||||||||||||||||||||||||||||||||||||||||||||||||||||

EIGHT tasty tricks for turning leftovers into breakfast

||||||||||||||||||||||||||||||||||||||||||||

1. If you have roasted vegetables or sautéed some greens the night before, whip any leftovers up with eggs, herbs and a bit of cheese to make a frittata, then bake in the oven.

2. Cook extra brown rice for dinner and make my brown rice coconut porridge (see page 156) to leave in the fridge overnight.

3. If you made pesto (page 241), keep some aside to eat it spread on rye toast the next morning, topped with a fried egg, or you could stir it into scrambled eggs.

4. If you have any leftover sautéed greens, chickpeas, black beans, half an avocado or even sautéed onions, try using them the next day in a breakfast wrap. Sprinkle spices, nutritional yeast and herbs on top for added flavour.

5. If you made polenta the night before, spread the leftovers out on a baking sheet overnight and refrigerate. In the morning, cut it into shapes, heat in a sauté or grill pan and cover with mashed fruit and a bit of maple syrup.

6. If you are roasting Portobello mushrooms for dinner, make a few extra and serve them with eggs the next morning.

7. Crack an egg into last night's tomato pasta sauce (see page 202) and gently poach the egg in the sauce until cooked through, then serve on rye toast.

8. Also remember you don't have to turn leftovers into anything – you can also just eat them as they are for breakfast. There are no rules!

'get up and go' breakfasts

If you find yourself strapped for time in the morning, it can often seem easier to grab a ready-made processed option, either from your cupboards (although hopefully you have purged them by now) or from a café on your way somewhere. But please believe me when I say that you can make a healthy breakfast just as quickly, and you'll be fuelled better and for much longer. The below quick, no-cook ideas are also good for anyone with limited ingredients, as they only require a handful of things, making them super simple and easy – and you can just pop them in an airtight container to go.

- A bowl of plain natural or coconut yoghurt with walnuts, goji berries, berries and chia seeds sprinkled on top.

- Chopped apple with nut butter as a dip. Or apple wedges covered in almond butter and rolled in gluten-free jumbo oats for added crunch and slow energy release.

- Toasted rye bread with half a mashed avocado, or a packet of oatcakes with a half an avocado to eat alongside. You can sprinkle salt, ground black pepper and chilli flakes on top for flavour.

- A wholegrain tortilla, spread with cashew butter, topped with chopped fruit and a sprinkle of chia seeds, then rolled up.

- Chopped celery (chop it the night before) stuffed with almond butter and scattered with chia seeds.

kids' breakfasts

For far too long now, sugar and breakfast have gone hand-in-hand when it comes to what children eat in the morning. Colourful packaging, promotional toys and vibrant television adverts don't help, but for the sake of their future health, we need to sever these associations. No matter how long it takes to reprogramme the way breakfast is defined in your household, it needs to be done.

Of course it is fun for kids on special occasions to enjoy a freshly baked croissant or muffin of their choice, but this has become the norm instead of the exception. It doesn't have to be this way.

Changing habits is never easy and it won't happen overnight, but what I would say, above and beyond everything, is to persevere. Don't give up just because you have a few bad mornings where your children refuse to have an egg scramble or porridge instead of their 'normal' breakfast. Eventually, change will happen – just like it has for you. Turn to page 144 in the next chapter for all my top tips on how to get your kids eating a healthy breakfast.

06
family:
eating nutritiously together

nyone with children will lament how fast time seems to go by when you have a growing family. In the blink of an eye your tiny infants sprout to school age and then into robust teenagers. Over the years, we hold great influence in nurturing their bodies and minds – and it is for this reason that this chapter is so important to me and is one I feel incredibly passionate about.

It is *our* responsibility as parents to educate our children about food – what real food is, what it means to fuel our bodies and minds, what effect food has on our bodies and what processed, manufactured food means. But the most important thing is to impart a love of cooking whole foods and teaching our children to enjoy the process of preparing and sharing a meal with loved ones.

This is where any learning should start: from a young age and in the kitchen, watching and helping you cook real foods. A healthy attitude and relationship with food in adulthood stems from a healthy attitude and relationship with food in childhood. It's never too young to start – and it's never too late either!

What I say in this chapter shouldn't be interpreted as an 'all-or-nothing' approach. I am well aware of how difficult it is to get children to do something they don't want to do, so be gentle with yourself (certainly you shouldn't think you're a failure if your kids won't eat quinoa on the first go, or even the second or third) and please don't expect miracles in the first week. This is a lifelong commitment and journey, so take it easy. Start by making small changes. That should be your main goal. Success is about trying new things, opening your children's palate to different ingredients and starting with simple swaps.

I have three kids, so I know very well how hard it is to find the time to sit down and read a whole chapter from start to finish. With that in mind, I've tried to make this chapter as approachable as possible. I have packed it with ideas and inspiration that you can either digest all at once or pick up bit-by-bit over time. I hope you'll try to implement some of my ideas into your family kitchen and, most importantly, that you stay open-minded – it may just rub off on your kids . . .

*supercharge soup*s
Making soup is a very easy way to pack a lot of goodness into one bowl. Present your kids with soups from a young age – they aren't just adult food – either as a main dish or as a side to something they love like sandwiches. Leeks, carrots, spinach, chickpeas, celery, kidney beans, kale, courgettes, squash and peppers can all be easily sautéed or roasted and then puréed with vegetable stock (not all at once, obviously!)

1. LEAD BY EXAMPLE

If you truly want to see your children eating nutritiously, then you really do need to take the lead on this one. My children first started eating chopped veggies and hummus because they saw me eating it as a snack after work; now it's one of their first choices when they're hungry. Actions do speak louder than words!

2. SIT DOWN

Sitting down to eat as a family with your children around a table is one of the most important things you can do in terms of encouraging a love of eating and sharing. Family mealtimes are an opportunity for the whole family to have a conversation together and connect over a meal. Eating at the dinner table collectively also reinforces to children that you're all in this together, caring about what you put in your bodies, paying thorough attention to the food that you nourish yourself with and finding enjoyment from eating it.

3. START WITH SMALLER CHANGES

Children will be far less keen to make changes if they see all their favourite foods disappearing at once, so make small switches gradually. If they are used to eating refined white pasta, try kamut, spelt, buckwheat or rice pasta – many of which have the same colour. If they like cereal with milk, give them almond or nut milk to begin with and then change their sugary cereal to a healthy version once they're used to it – perhaps Low-sugar granola (see page 168) or Brown rice coconut porridge (see page 156).

|||||||||||||||||||||||||||||||||||||||||||||||||||||||||||||||||||||||||||||||||||||||||||||||||||||||||||||||||||||||||||||||||||

FIVE baby step examples to try

||||||||||||||||||||||||||||||||||||||||

- If your kids like fried food, first try healthy chicken and fish fingers (see page 148), then try tamari baked tofu (see page 211)

- If your kids like crisps, first try root-vegetable crisps, then try kale crisps (they're available to buy in supermarkets and lots of health-food stores).

- If your kids like burgers, try black bean burgers (see page 208).

- If your kids like sweetened dried fruit, first try vegetable crisps, then try seasoned dried seaweed.

- If your kids like pastries and muffins, first try banana, pecan and cacao nib muffins (see page 223), then try sunshine sunflower balls (see page 220).

4. CLEAR OUT YOUR CUPBOARDS

You can't have an argument with your kids about why they can't snack on a chocolate bar or have croissants or sugary cereals for breakfast if there aren't any in the house. You hold the power to decide what's in your kitchen – use that power wisely.

5. PLAN AHEAD

For busy parents, part of the difficulty in eating well as a family is simply lack of time. Sticking a ready meal in the oven often seems like the easier option. However, with a little planning and preparation it doesn't have to be this way. Turn back to Chapter 2, on *Getting organised* (see page 34), for all my tips and advice on how devoting a little time to planning and prep each week will be such a lifesaver when it comes to feeding your family quickly, easily and healthily.

6. NO 'BIG DEAL' EATING

It's human nature for kids to rebel against their parents – at least to a degree. If you constantly talk about how you are trying new healthy ingredients and you aren't sure they are going to like them but they'd better eat them because they are good for them, and so forth, it just directs too much attention to the wrong thoughts. They'll only use it as ammunition to wind you up about not wanting to eat healthy food. Focus on the positives instead, and just present them with new foods.

7. REWARDING REWARDS

Food equals reward was the sum many of us were taught as children. We need to start finding other ways of rewarding our little ones. Let them watch a movie, sleep in your bed, have a friend over or go on a day trip that they're excited about.

8. SEEK THEIR INPUT

It is important that we talk to children about what they are eating. Whenever I present something new or amend a well-loved recipe slightly, I ask them to tell me what they taste. Do they taste anything new? What would they put in it to make it better? This simply makes them think about how you create foods. Of course, this often deteriorates into 'I think you put fish eyeballs, worm juice and dragon scales in this', but that's okay too – keep it light. Mealtimes shouldn't be a science lesson, just an appreciation of real food.

dairy direction

If your kids aren't ready to try plant-based milks, that's okay but try to always buy organic dairy milk as it means the animals producing it have not been exposed to chemicals and growth hormones — either on the land they live on or in the food they eat. For more on organic farming see page 30.

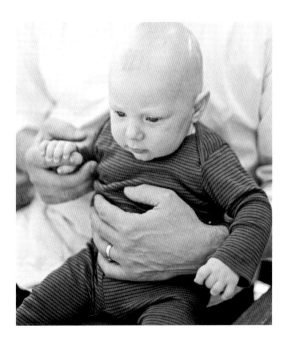

01 TIMING IS EVERYTHING

Try new things with your kids when they are most hungry. I cut down my children's snack intake before they are meant to be eating; if they sit down for a meal already half-full, they are much less likely to try something new.

02 CONTROL FREAKS

Create meals and mealtime scenarios where children feel they have control over their food. Ask kids at the beginning of the week to choose what they would like to eat from a list of ideas you have written out. Or they can look through cookbooks with you and make requests for specific recipes throughout the week.

03 KEEP IT FAMILIAR

Refer to foods using familiar names – don't give healthy foods new 'weird' names that draw attention to their difference. When I offer 'cookies', 'brownies' or 'ice cream' my children come running. The name has convinced them that they want some, even though they are eating a healthier version of the original.

04 BE STEALTHY

No matter how much you try, sometimes children just won't budge when it comes to trying new vegetables. I'm not encouraging deception per se; however, it isn't a bad thing to sneak them in whenever possible to ensure your child is eating a more balanced, nutrient-dense diet. This is especially important with fussy eaters.

FIVE sneaky ways that work with kids

- Hide puréed kale and spinach in soups and tomato pasta sauces – they'll get the goodness without knowing it.

- Add chia seeds to muesli, smoothies and muffins (see page 223 for my banana, pecan and cacao nib muffins).

- Mix greens – such as spinach, kale or chard – chopped tomatoes and chopped peppers with eggs to make omelettes.

- Smoothies made with kale, avocado and courgette are a great way of giving your kids lots of veggies without them noticing. The sweetness of a banana, apple or berries hides the veg.

- Make my rainbow fried rice on page 198. Use whatever veggies you have in the fridge – the end result is always a hit.

05   KEEP AN EYE OUT FOR HIDDEN SUGAR

Knowing where to cut sugar from your kids' diet is obvious in the case of chocolate bars, fizzy drinks and sweets. However, sugar can hide! Fruit juices, 'healthy' cereal, canned fruit, snack bars, dried fruit, fruit-flavoured yoghurts, tomato sauces, ketchup, salad dressings and soups can all be high in hidden sugar, so start reading the ingredients labels of everything you choose. (See pages 98–121 for more on this.)

06   NEVER UNDERESTIMATE YOUR KIDS

Children aren't born only liking plain and sweet foods, so broaden their horizons and get them to try a new ingredient each week; it's also a great way to involve them in what they eat. Introduce herbs, spices and new flavours with the attitude that they will like them (remember, they learn by example) instead of convincing yourself they won't before you even give it a go.

07   ATTACK BREAKFAST

Your children's breakfast is the meal that will start them with the right kind of energy for the day ahead. Reforming this mealtime means no more sweetened fruit yoghurt, jam on toast or cereals with sugar. Savoury foods, good grains and plants should be the focus. Make a plan with your children to try one new breakfast option every week, and include them in the menu idea and shopping process as much as possible. Give them three options to choose from.

||||||||||||||||||||||||||||||||||||||||||||||||||||||||||||||||||||||||||||||||||||||||||||||||||||||||||||||||||||||||||||||||||||||||

cutting out cereal

If your kids love cereal then don't take it away completely at first. I suggest starting by limiting how many days per week they can have it and then gradually decreasing the number. And, as a start, try to choose a healthier cereal with less sugar! Most importantly, try some new breakfast ideas that might pique their interest on the other days. Here are some ideas for tasty breakfasts for kids:

- **Plain yoghurt with chopped fruit** (instead of fruit-flavoured yoghurt) – let them do the mashing.
- **An unsweetened rice cake** with peanut butter or almond butter to make an open 'sandwich'.
- **Overnight oats** (see page 159) served in a jar.
- **Fried eggs with multigrain toast** and (if they like it) chopped avocado.
- **Half an avocado** with an egg baked in the middle.
- **Brown rice coconut porridge** (recipe on page 156).

||||||||||||||||||||||||||||||||||||||||||||||||||||||||||||||||||||||||||||||||||||||||||||||||||||||||||||||||||||||||||||||||||||||||

08 THE LUNCH BOX HUSTLE

Don't forget to keep your kids well fuelled during the day as well as when they're with you. Serving mini portions always works well in lunch boxes. You could try: cubes of cheese; sliced celery and carrot sticks with a small tub of hummus; grapes; a mini portion of Chia seed pudding (see page 171 for recipe); flax crackers or rye bread; any leftovers from the night before, such as roasted vegetables or a portion of wild rice and something delicious and naturally sweet, such as a Coconut spirulina energy ball (see page 224 for the recipe). Try not to give them anything that will be hard to eat, such as a banana if they find it hard to peel themselves, or that will look unappetising by lunch, such as avocado or chopped apple, which will go brown.

09 STICK TO WATER

Trying to cut down on sugary items in your children's life can be difficult, but fruit juice should be one of the key places to start, as there is no reason to quench their thirst with sugar – they need to be drinking water. Start by flavouring pitchers of water with sliced ginger or lemons, blackberries, cucumber or orange slices to make it more appealing to them. Or make ice cubes with lemon and herbs in them so they can throw them in a glass of water at any time.

10 MAKE GOODNESS ACCESSIBLE

Always have chopped veggies and washed fruit available in the fridge (at their height if possible) so they can reach for healthy snacks without a lot of assistance. Make it known that they can eat these whenever they are hungry – except for the one hour before dinner; that way they won't lose their appetite.

mommy's magic milkshakes

When I give my kids a special dessert as a treat, we make milkshakes with REAL ice cream but I put the following in the blender too: coconut milk (unsweetened; from a carton), 1 banana, ½ an avocado, 1 tablespoon of flaxseeds and 1 tablespoon of chia seeds. I've never once heard a complaint about my milkshakes, which makes for a very happy mommy!

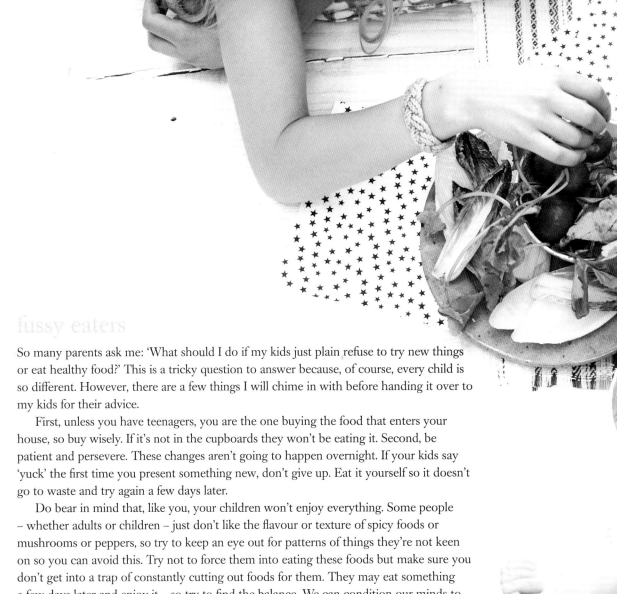

fussy eaters

So many parents ask me: 'What should I do if my kids just plain refuse to try new things or eat healthy food?' This is a tricky question to answer because, of course, every child is so different. However, there are a few things I will chime in with before handing it over to my kids for their advice.

First, unless you have teenagers, you are the one buying the food that enters your house, so buy wisely. If it's not in the cupboards they won't be eating it. Second, be patient and persevere. These changes aren't going to happen overnight. If your kids say 'yuck' the first time you present something new, don't give up. Eat it yourself so it doesn't go to waste and try again a few days later.

Do bear in mind that, like you, your children won't enjoy everything. Some people – whether adults or children – just don't like the flavour or texture of spicy foods or mushrooms or peppers, so try to keep an eye out for patterns of things they're not keen on so you can avoid this. Try not to force them into eating these foods but make sure you don't get into a trap of constantly cutting out foods for them. They may eat something a few days later and enjoy it – so try to find the balance. We can condition our minds to like ingredients over time. And don't forget that our palates change as we get older, so something your kids may really dislike when younger can become a favourite food as they get older. Keep introducing these ingredients back into their diet every couple of months.

Lastly, don't give in quickly and make them something else. They have to know this is the meal – full stop. Put the meal on the table and leave it there. Keep it in the fridge if they don't eat it – for when they inevitably say they're hungry later – and then give it to them again. It can take up to five to 10 times of being exposed to a new flavour before children up to the age of 5 years will accept it. Persistence is key and just remember – you are in charge.

Quite often I hear the advice to 'get your kids involved in the kitchen' yet that's easier said than done in everyday life, given how busy it can be. However, wherever possible it is important for kids to participate in the planning and making of meals. Here are some of the practical ways I do it in our home:

1. Don't try to force involvement on weekdays when there's homework and chores to get done. Do it on the weekends when both you and your children have more time.

2. Children will be more engaged – and useful – if you give them tasks they can easily help with: tearing herbs and lettuce, grating cheese, using a salad spinner, whisking wet ingredients, squeezing lemons, counting out a precise number of ingredients, rolling doughs – my cashew thumbprint cookies (see page 231 and opposite) are perfect for this, and, of course, using cookie cutters to make shapes. It's also very important to have a step stool for little ones so they can be at counter level and truly be part of the action.

3. Make them responsible for a certain element of a dish and explain how their role works as part of the meal overall. When it all comes together, they feel a real sense of achievement. For example, if they help you time the pasta or stir the sauce, then make it known at the dinner table that the reason it tastes so delicious is because they helped you with that part.

4. Kids love to create their own dishes. Burritos, tacos, wraps, brown rice bowls (see page 211) and rice paper rolls (see page 191) will allow them to choose how they want to fill their meal. Chop up all the ingredients and put them in individual bowls, then let your kids decide what they want – the more healthy fillings, the healthier the outcome.

5. Talk about where specific ingredients come from (or have them guess) when you are eating. Does cauliflower come from trees? Are avocados fruits or vegetables? This just gets them thinking about the sources of the food they eat.

6. Ask their opinion about recipes. My kids are the 'official taste testers' in our house. If I am ever creating a new recipe or trying something out before we have friends over, I give it to them first and tell them they are in charge of deciding if it's worth the effort. It makes them feel involved and important in the kitchen and *always* ensures I get honest feedback.

7. Sometimes, when I am stuck for ideas on what to cook at home, my kids and I pull out a cookbook and everyone has to close their eyes. Then we randomly pick a page each – whatever we blindly fall on is our choice. Once we have all made our picks, we choose one to try – whoever gets their recipe chosen is the winner.

8. Overall just keep it light, encourage involvement, but don't force it. Help them find the fun in helping in the kitchen.

after school snack ideas

School is hard work, and kids are always super hungry at pick-up time, so it's the perfect time to revive their energy and fuel the rest of their day with nutritiously dense snack choices. These are ideas that I use regularly – mix and match them as you wish.

♡ Chunks of cheese with celery and carrots

♡ My roasted flavoured nuts *(see page 218)*

♡ Tamari ginger roasted chickpeas *(see page 219)*

♡ Rice cake 'sandwiches' with nut butter

♡ Trail mix

♡ Dried seaweed snacks

♡ Hummus and raw veggies

♡ Cooked edamame *(see page 92)*

♡ Carrot sticks with no-sugar peanut sauce *(see page 247)* for dipping

♡ Hard-boiled eggs *(see page 47)*

♡ Chopped celery with goats' cheese in the middle

♡ Cucumber with yoghurt (spiced with dill, mint and turmeric) as a dip

♡ Apple slices with cinnamon

♡ Chopped apple to dip in almond or peanut butter

♡ Chopped apple with slices of Cheddar cheese

♡ Smoothie in a takeaway cup

♡ Pot of low-sugar granola *(see page 168)*

♡ Pieces of fresh coconut

♡ Matcha cacao macaroons *(see page 222)*

♡ Cashew thumbprint cookies *(see page 231)*

Children love food that is colourful, bite-sized or cut into fun shapes. Here are a few ideas that always get a smile in my house:

- KEBABS – i.e. anything on a skewer – are always hugely popular. You can do this with chunks of chicken, fish, tofu and veggies. Roast them with a drizzle of extra virgin olive oil, salt and pepper in an oven set at 180°C/gas 4 for about 30 minutes depending on what you are cooking. Courgettes, peppers, onions, Portobello mushrooms, tomatoes, aubergine, fennel and asparagus all work well too.

- TOOTHPICKS – we stick them in everything: cubes of cheese, pieces of roasted veggies, chunks of raw vegetables or fruit, and use them to hold a sandwich together.

- PORTABLE FOODS – kids seem to like anything more when it is presented in a colourful bag or a box. Maybe it feels like they're heading out on a fun adventure or maybe they like the control of holding their own food. Whatever the reason, buy cute little bags and boxes (IKEA has great ones) and serve as many healthy foods as possible in this way.

- POPSICLES – when you have leftover smoothie mixture (or you can just make extra), pour it into popsicle moulds and freeze it (see page 238 for lots of popsicle ideas).

- FACES – either you or they can be the artist, but making smiley faces out of ingredients always seems to take the focus away from 'I don't like this' conversations. With boiled eggs, put some crayons nearby so they can draw faces on the shells before cracking them open.

- BITES – rolling foods into bite-sized amounts means they are fun to pop in their mouths and they never feel overwhelming. Try my Broccoli 'meatballs' on page 201.

- STRAWS – if I use fun straws my kids instantly want to drink their smoothies. You can buy all kinds online from stripy to metal to patterned.

- POPCORN – store-bought popcorn is full of additives, salt and/or sugar but you can easily make your own; just buy a bag of popping corn and follow the packet instructions.

Remember it's never too late. Attitudes towards food and eating are learned from an early age so, regardless of how old your children are, the key is to start making changes as soon as possible – start today! Equally, it's never too early to start. Get them used to the savoury side of life in the first six months after they've been weaned. If you didn't do this, don't worry. Just start changing habits at whatever stage your children are at. Don't ever feel like it's a lost cause.

07
recipes

brown rice coconut porridge

Nothing feels more efficient than using leftovers to make one of the yummiest breakfasts around. This feels so much more decadent than 'normal' porridge, and it is a great way to break up the monotony of any morning routine. It's rich, it's creamy and it almost feels like dessert at 7am – almost. Although this is a great prep-ahead dish (you can mix everything together the night before), you can also make it in the morning – just try to let it simmer a bit longer so the flavours have time to mingle.

serves 3

200g cooked brown
   rice (uncooked weight
   is 100g; I generally use
   leftovers from dinner)
250ml coconut milk
   (unsweetened; from a
   carton)
3 tbsp desiccated
   coconut
   (unsweetened)
30g plain cashews
   (not roasted, salted
   or sweetened),
   roughly chopped
pinch of ground cloves
½ tsp ground nutmeg
½ tsp ground cinnamon
½ tsp vanilla extract
1 tbsp raw clear honey
   or maple syrup, to
   serve (optional)
handful of berries,
   to serve (optional)

In a mixing bowl, combine the cooked brown rice with the coconut milk, desiccated coconut, cashews, cloves, nutmeg, cinnamon and vanilla extract. Mix well and then pop it in the fridge and leave overnight.

Heat the following morning for 5 minutes over a medium to gentle heat, ensuring that the rice is thoroughly reheated. Drizzle the honey or maple syrup over the top, if using, but try it without first. Finish by sprinkling over the berries, if using.

We officially call overnight oats 'cookie dough' in our house – that's how popular they are. And they're popular with me too because they're fast! All you do is put all the ingredients in a large jar and give it a shake, or just use a bowl, stir and cover. Then pop the oats in the refrigerator overnight and they are perfection the next morning.

I never use sweetener in these recipes because I think they are sweet enough, but if you must add a little, do it in the morning after you have tasted it – don't just assume you'll need it sweeter.

I make the peanut butter and banana version for weekend brunches. It even works as a dessert if you add a few carob chips or cacao nibs.

serves 2

150g jumbo or rolled oats (gluten-free if possible)
2 tbsp almond butter
375ml coconut milk (unsweetened; from a carton)
2 tsp desiccated coconut (unsweetened)
2 tsp chia seeds
½ tsp ground cinnamon

serves 2

100g rolled oats (gluten-free if possible)
250ml coconut milk (unsweetened; from a carton)
90g frozen blueberries
2 tsp desiccated coconut (unsweetened)
1 tbsp flaked almonds
½ tsp ground cinnamon
1 tsp pure almond extract

serves 2

100g steel-cut oats or rolled oats (gluten-free if possible)
2 tbsp cashew butter
250ml coconut milk (unsweetened; from a carton)
50g raspberries (frozen or fresh)
2 Medjool dates, pitted and chopped
2 tsp chia seeds
1 tsp vanilla extract

serves 2

125g rolled oats (gluten-free if possible)
250ml almond milk (unsweetened)
1 ripe banana, roughly chopped
4 tbsp peanut butter (unsweetened)
½ tsp salt (if peanut butter is unsalted)
1 tbsp chia seeds

courgette 'bread' porridge

Don't be put off by the idea of having courgette for breakfast. We all need to open our minds to different nutritious breakfast options and this one is positively top. We are big fans of courgette bread in our house so I came up with a way to use the same flavours in a porridge. It's a good choice for a weekend morning when you've got a bit more time, since you need to cook the porridge for about 30 minutes.

serves 2–3

240ml coconut water

240ml coconut milk (unsweetened; from a carton)

1 tsp ground cinnamon, plus extra for dusting

1/8 tsp ground cloves

1/2 tsp ground ginger

1/4 tsp ground nutmeg

1/4 tsp salt

75g jumbo oats (gluten-free if possible)

65g raisins

140g courgette (about 1 large courgette), finely grated

ground cinnamon, to serve (optional)

maple syrup or raw honey, to serve (optional)

Bring the coconut water, coconut milk, spices and salt to a boil in a medium saucepan.

Stir in the oats, reduce the heat to medium and cook for about 5 minutes, stirring frequently.

Add in the raisins and courgette, reduce the heat further and simmer for another 15–20 minutes or until it reaches your desired porridge consistency, stirring every 5 minutes or so.

Serve with a dusting of cinnamon or maybe a drizzle of maple syrup or honey.

sweet quinoa and coconut morning pud

This porridge will delight your morning palate. It's packed with vibrant flavours, soothing warm aromas and dense, gluten-free grains that will give you lasting energy for the day ahead. If you have any left over, don't throw it out; it's great served cold too as an afternoon snack.

serves 4–6

500ml coconut
  milk(unsweetened;
  from a carton), plus
  an extra splash for
  serving
2 Medjool dates, pitted
  and finely chopped
½ tsp ground cardamom
1 star anise
180g quinoa, rinsed
100g millet or amaranth,
  rinsed
1 ripe banana, mashed
1 tsp vanilla extract
2 tbsp desiccated
  coconut
  (unsweetened)
handful of blueberries
  or raspberries, to serve

In a medium-sized saucepan, bring the coconut milk to a boil. Add the dates, cardamom, star anise, quinoa and millet or amaranth. Cover with a tight-fitting lid and gently simmer for 20 minutes, until the liquid is absorbed.

Remove from the heat. Add the banana, vanilla extract and desiccated coconut and give it a good stir. Then replace the lid and leave it to sit for another 5 minutes. Remove the star anise.

Once ready, serve with blueberries or raspberries.

gluten-free buckwheat pancakes, *three ways*

Buckwheat flour is a great base for gluten-free pancakes because it's sturdy enough to hold its shape well and has a unique nutty flavour, which works well with sweet and savoury. So here are three of my favourite versions.

The original, 'plain' version tastes delicious topped with almond or cashew butter, coconut butter, fresh fruit and/or maple syrup (remember, just use a bit). The green pancakes call for a savoury topping – try a poached egg, avocado and grilled tomatoes or a soft goats' cheese. The choice for the red one is up to you; these beetroot beauties are delicious served either as a savoury dish with my Silly dill dip (page 244) or sweet with my Cashew cream (page 232).

THE ORIGINAL

makes 12–14 pancakes

300g buckwheat flour
2 tsp baking powder
500ml almond milk (unsweetened)
2 tsp vanilla extract
1–2 tsp maca powder (optional)
pinch of ground cinnamon or nutmeg (optional)
50g unsalted butter or 3 tbsp melted coconut oil

In a bowl, mix together the buckwheat flour and baking powder. Make a well in the centre of the flour mixture and gradually pour in the almond milk, whisking all the time to make a smooth batter. Then add the vanilla extract. If you fancy, you can also add the maca powder and/or cinnamon or nutmeg.

Cook the pancakes in batches over a medium heat. Place a knob of butter or a tablespoon of coconut oil in a large non-stick frying pan to coat the base. Ladle around 4 tablespoons of batter for each pancake into the pan; you should be able to cook 3 pancakes per batch, before needing to add a little more butter or oil to coat the pan between batches.

Cook each pancake for 1–2 minutes or until bubbles appear on the surface of the pancake, then flip and cook on the other side until golden and the pancakes are cooked through. Keep the cooked pancakes warm on a plate in a low oven while you cook the remainder. ➤

SPINACH AND LEEK 'GREEN' PANCAKES

makes 14–16 pancakes

1 leek, thinly sliced

4 tbsp extra virgin olive oil or coconut oil, for frying

2 big handfuls of spinach

1 batch of The original pancake batter (see page 163) but omitting the vanilla, maca and spices

1 handful coriander, finely chopped

1 tsp cumin

salt and pepper

In a medium-sized pan, quickly sauté your sliced leeks in a tablespoon of the oil until they are soft. Transfer to a bowl.

Then throw your spinach in the same pan and wilt very quickly on a low heat; this should only take 1–2 minutes. Remove from the pan, chop finely and transfer to the bowl with the leeks.

Once you've made the pancake batter, simply stir in the cooked leeks, spinach, coriander and cumin, then season. Cook the pancakes (as described on page 163) in a little olive oil or coconut oil, flip and serve.

BEETROOT AND COCONUT 'RED' PANCAKES

makes 8–10 pancakes

2 small beetroot (raw or pre-boiled)

200g buckwheat flour

1 tsp baking powder

2 medium eggs

2 tbsp maple syrup

1 tsp vanilla extract

250ml coconut milk (unsweetened; from a carton)

3–4 tbsp extra virgin olive oil or coconut oil, for roasting and cooking

If using raw beetroot, preheat the oven to 200°C/gas 6, then peel the beetroot and cut each one into four. Place in a baking dish, drizzle with olive oil and bake for 20–30 minutes, until cooked through. If using pre-boiled beetroot, simply cut each into four pieces.

Put the flour and baking powder into a large bowl. In a separate bowl, mix together the eggs, maple syrup and vanilla extract.

Let the beetroot cool a bit, then transfer it to a blender or food processor. Add the coconut milk and whizz until the mixture is completely smooth. Add this purée to the egg mixture and whisk until combined. Gradually add this to the flour mixture, whisking all the time. Mix well until you have a smooth batter.

Cook the pancakes (as described on page 163) in a little olive oil or coconut oil, flip and serve.

I love granola, my kids love granola, we all love granola, so I am always trying out new oat-based concoctions and this one gets a household thumbs up. It tastes delicious served with almond or coconut milk, or with coconut yoghurt or plain Greek yoghurt for something a bit richer, and chopped fruit on top. I also love it dry as a snack; I often put a few handfuls in a plastic container and take it out and about with me. Leave out the cranberries if you are trying to go as low-sugar as possible.

serves 4–6/makes 325g

200g jumbo oats
  (gluten-free if
  possible)
1 handful (around 30g)
  pumpkin seeds
1 tbsp flaxseeds
1 handful (around 10g)
  coconut flakes
½ tsp ground nutmeg
1 tsp ground
  cinnamon
1 handful (around 35g)
  plain walnuts, almonds
  or cashews (whichever
  you prefer), roughly
  chopped
3 tsp maple syrup
2 tbsp coconut oil,
  melted
2 tbsp coconut water
drop of vanilla extract
2–3 tsp dried
  cranberries (optional)

Preheat the oven to 160°C/gas 3 and line a baking sheet with baking parchment.

Mix together the oats, pumpkin seeds, flaxseeds, coconut flakes, nutmeg, cinnamon and walnuts, almonds or cashews in a large mixing bowl with a spoon or your hands.

In a small saucepan, heat up the maple syrup, coconut oil, coconut water and vanilla extract until boiling. Take off the hob and carefully stir into the mixing bowl with the dry ingredients. Use a spoon to mix as it will be hot!

Spread the granola evenly over the prepared baking sheet, then bake in the oven for 20 minutes or until golden, stirring the granola after 10 minutes so it doesn't catch at the edges and cooks evenly.

Remove from the oven and, if using, add the cranberries and stir into the mixture. Cool and store in an airtight container for up to 2 weeks.

chia seed pudding, *three ways*

Chia seeds can be added to a catalogue of recipes for an added health supercharge. I like to mix mine into smoothies, porridge, scrambled eggs, muffins and omelettes, among other recipes. But one great way to use these little balls of goodness is in a chia seed pudding which is not really a dessert; it's more like a tapioca/porridge mix. Chia puddings make a super simple breakfast or can be an afternoon treat – all you need to do is soak the chia seeds with almond or coconut milk in a bowl or jar, then add in anything extra for flavour. Give it all a good whisk together and then pop in the fridge for a few hours or overnight. The possibilities for these are endless but here are three of my favourite combinations:

serves 4

150g chia seeds
750ml almond or coconut
  milk (unsweetened; from
  a carton)
2 tbsp desiccated coconut
20g flaked almonds,
  toasted, plus extra to
  decorate
60g frozen blueberries
  (use frozen as they turn
  everything bright purple
  – fun!)
½ tsp ground cinnamon
½ tsp vanilla extract

serves 4

150g chia seeds
750ml almond or coconut
  milk (unsweetened; from
  a carton)
3 Medjool dates, pitted and
  finely chopped
½ tsp ground cardamom
½ tsp vanilla extract
pumpkin seeds, to decorate

serves 4

150g chia seeds
750ml almond or coconut
  milk (unsweetened; from
  a carton)
1 tbsp almond butter
1 medium apple, grated
70g pomegranate seeds,
  plus extra to decorate

Eggs are of course the base of any scramble, but the magic of making them supercharged and delicious is up to you. These meals are never boring, always nutritious and wonderfully quick. You can whip them up in minutes (especially if you have prepared your veggies ahead on prep day).

serves 1 as a hearty breakfast or brunch

For your egg base:

3 eggs (use only one of the yolks if you want to make it lighter)

4 tbsp coconut milk (unsweetened; from a carton)

¼ tsp salt

salt and pepper

Whisk your eggs, coconut milk and salt together vigorously in a mixing bowl. Then pour this into a heated sauté pan and let it start to set a bit.

Using a spatula, scramble your eggs until cooked to your liking (I like mine quite runny), then season with salt and pepper and add your chosen toppings.

Optional toppings

- Cooked black beans and salsa (or finely chopped tomatoes if you don't have salsa)
- Steamed spinach and feta cheese
- Roasted tomatoes (you can make these in advance)
- Swiss chard and chopped sun-dried tomatoes
- Steamed asparagus and pesto (see my recipes on page 241)
- Sautéed mushrooms and thyme

my avocado on toast

Instagram's darling, avocado on toast, never seems to bore anyone – least of all me. In my opinion a wholesome piece of bread smothered in avocado (plus a drizzle of olive oil and sprinkle of salt) is one of the most perfect pairings of simplicity and flavour ever created. And you can whip it up in the time it takes to toast a piece of bread. This works as a wonderful breakfast, lunch, dinner or midnight snack.

As I'm here to excite your plant-based palate, here are six new mouth-watering ways to try this nutritious meal. Because avocados have a mild flavour, they work well with many different ingredients. The base is always the same for me: a thick slice of the best bread you can get – maybe it's multigrain, maybe it's rye or maybe it's gluten-free – whatever it is, place it in the toaster until golden. For the topping, give some of these combinations a try.

serves 4

coconut oil, for
  spreading
multigrain, rye or
  gluten-free bread,
  toasted
¼–½ avocado per slice
  of bread
chilli flakes, to serve
  (optional)
salt

Spread the thinnest layer of coconut oil over your warm toast and smash (I prefer the smash technique as opposed to small cubes) ¼–½ avocado flesh on each piece of bread.

Then sprinkle with a bit of salt and chilli flakes if you like the heat.

Optional toppings

- Sun-dried tomatoes and pitted black olives
- Black beans and goats' cheese
- Alfalfa sprouts and toasted or raw sunflower seeds
- Watercress leaves (stems removed) and pesto (see my recipes on page 241)
- Sliced tomatoes, sliced red onion and chopped fresh basil leaves
- Feta cheese and pumpkin seeds

feel the beet
smoothie
(see page 178)

maca smoothie
(see page 178)

superfood
smoothie
(see page 178)

If there is one way to get a whole lot of nutrients in a quick and compact serving for breakfast, it's with a smoothie. They couldn't be easier to make; you throw everything in a blender and whizz them together. I have given you some of my favourite smoothie recipes to try over the next few pages, however, the beauty of smoothies is your ability to be creative. It's easy to become a pro so you can use the ingredients you have to whizz up something tasty at any time. I use a basic structure, outlined below, which will keep you on track, but there really is no right or wrong way to fill your blender. You'll be penning your own recipes before you know it.

Of course I'm not a supporter of deception, but one fantastic characteristic of smoothies is their ability to conceal many nutritious ingredients that you may not otherwise be used to eating for breakfast – for example, kale, courgette, spinach, avocado and sweet potato. Once combined with a handful of fruit, some coconut water or plant milk, and perhaps some flavoured plant-based protein powder, you (and your children) won't be able to name the individual ingredients – you'll simply have a delicious creamy mixture to enjoy. And that's morning success if ever there was some.

my smoothie building blocks

When I make smoothies, I think about creating them from three basic groups of ingredients; the base, the bulk and the extras. If you follow these principles you will create terrific smoothies time after time.

1. Base

These are the liquids that create the volume and texture of your smoothie. Too much base and your smoothie will be too runny; too little and it will be too thick to suck down a straw, which is no fun first thing in the morning.

Your base can be a plant milk or you can use coconut water and fresh water. I usually use a mix of half water or coconut water and half plant-based milk.

2. Bulk

This is made up of the vegetables, fruits, nuts and seeds that will give your smoothie its heartiness. Of course, most importantly, I add veggies. I regularly use spinach, kale, beetroot, courgette and avocado. For a little sweetness I use apples, pears, a banana or blueberries most often, as they work really well, but I never use more than one apple or one pear because of the sugar content. A strong blender will whizz everything, so don't be afraid of throwing in a handful of almonds, sunflower, pumpkin or chia seeds (though watch as chia seeds swell so you might need to adjust your liquid quantity), or goji berries to add extra bulk, good fats and nutrients.

3. Extras

Finally, you can add powders, superfood extracts and supplements. I have given you a list on page 89 of my favourite supplements you can add to your cooking, and they all work brilliantly in smoothies. They will give you a whole heap of extra nutrients, antioxidants and vitamins. They're available to buy from most health-food shops.

FEEL THE BEET SMOOTHIE

serves 3

1 small raw beetroot, peeled and diced
2 handfuls (about 60g) spinach
2 oranges, peeled
250ml water
125ml coconut water
juice of ½ lemon
2 tbsp chia seeds
1 tsp lucuma (optional)

Blend the beetroot, spinach, oranges and water until smooth. Then add the remaining ingredients and blend again before serving.

MACA SMOOTHIE

serves 2

500ml almond or coconut milk
    (unsweetened; from a carton)
50g almond butter
1 tsp ground cinnamon
1 banana, broken into 2.5cm pieces,
    then frozen
½ tsp vanilla extract
1–3 tsp maca powder, depending on
    preference
1 handful ice cubes

Whizz the ingredients together in a blender, then serve.

SUPERFOOD SMOOTHIE

serves 2–3

250ml coconut milk (unsweetened;
    from a carton)
125ml coconut water
125ml water
1 tbsp almond butter
20g kale (frozen or fresh), stalks removed
60g blueberries
½ avocado, pitted and peeled
1 tbsp chia seeds
1 tsp–1 tbsp green powder (to taste)

Whizz the ingredients together in a blender, then serve.

TROPICAL GREEN SMOOTHIE

serves 4

250ml almond milk (unsweetened)
500ml water
70g strawberries (frozen or fresh)
1 handful (about 30g) spinach
20g kale (frozen or fresh), stalks removed
1 banana
2 lemons (or limes), peeled
85g pineapple (fresh or frozen)
1 tbsp hemp seeds
1 tbsp flaxseeds

Whizz the ingredients together in a blender, then serve.

APPLE CRUMBLE SMOOTHIE

serves 2

125ml coconut water
250ml water
juice of 1 lemon
1 apple, cored, unpeeled and roughly
 chopped
1 handful (about 30g) spinach
50g rolled oats (gluten-free if possible)
1cm ginger, peeled
½ tbsp ground cinnamon
½ tsp ground nutmeg
1 scoop of vanilla-flavoured protein powder

Whizz the ingredients together in a
blender, then serve.

BASIL BEAUTY SMOOTHIE

serves 3

500ml almond milk (unsweetened)
2 handfuls (about 60g) spinach
1 large apple, cored, unpeeled and roughly
 chopped
1 banana
½ avocado, pitted and peeled
1 lemon, peeled
15 basil leaves

Whizz the ingredients together in a
blender, then serve.

CHOCOLATE-FIX SMOOTHIE

serves 3

500ml almond milk (unsweetened)
1½ handfuls (about 45g) spinach
2 bananas
½ avocado, peeled and pitted
4 Medjool dates, pitted
12 mint leaves
2 tbsp cacao powder

Whizz the ingredients together in a
blender, then serve.

GREEN GOODNESS SMOOTHIE

serves 2

250ml water
40g kale (fresh or frozen), stalks removed
2 large stalks of celery, chopped
½ cucumber, chopped
⅓ grapefruit
170g pineapple (fresh or frozen)

Whizz the ingredients together in a
blender, then serve.

breakfast & smoothies **179**

calgary's cauliflower couscous

Cauliflower 'couscous' or 'rice' is having its moment, and you may have come across a version or two of this recipe before, but this is my favourite combination of flavours and textures. I just had to include it in my book as it's something I make a lot of at home because it is so quick and simple and is a brilliant plant-packed, gluten-free alternative to using the grain itself.

serves 4 as a main, or 6–8 as a side

1 large cauliflower
   (about 750g after
   trimming)
3 tbsp extra virgin
   olive oil
½ tsp ground turmeric
½ tsp ground cinnamon
½ tsp ground nutmeg
grated zest of 1 lemon
juice of ½ lemon
15 mint leaves, roughly
   chopped
60g pistachios, toasted
   and roughly chopped
4 spring onions,
   chopped
100g goats' cheese,
   crumbled
1 x 400g can chickpeas,
   drained and rinsed
½ pomegranate, seeds
   removed (optional)
juice of 1 lime
salt and pepper

Core and cut the cauliflower into medium florets. Blitz the florets in a food processor until they resemble couscous. Do it in two batches if the food processor is more than three-quarters full. Don't over-blend, otherwise it will become puréed – that's baby food, not couscous.

Add 2 tablespoons of olive oil and fluff with a fork, then season with the salt, pepper, turmeric, cinnamon and nutmeg. Then add all the remaining ingredients except the lime juice and toss together. Add additional olive oil, salt and pepper if necessary. Pour the lime juice over the top.

buckwheat tabbouleh

This is a very simple, fresh and crunchy salad. I call it a 'handful' salad as there's nothing too precise about it: just easy handfuls of fragrant herbs – perfect for leisurely, laidback meals. You can toss a dressing through it too if you want but I like the simplicity of topping it only with lemon, salt and pepper. And, remember, buckwheat has nothing to do with wheat (see page 66), so this is completely gluten-free.

serves 4 as a main, or 6–8 as a side

150g raw buckwheat
  groats
300ml vegetable stock
2 medium tomatoes
¼ medium red onion
1 medium cucumber
1 spring onion
1 handful of flat-leaf
  parsley
1 handful of mint
2 handfuls of basil
125g peas (frozen or
  fresh)
30g pine nuts
juice of 1 lemon
2 tbsp extra virgin
  olive oil
salt and pepper

Cook the buckwheat groats in the vegetable stock in a saucepan set over a medium heat, until the liquid is completely absorbed – it should take about 15–20 minutes – or simply cook the buckwheat as per the packet instructions.

While cooking the buckwheat, finely chop the tomatoes, onion, cucumber and spring onion and roughly chop all of the herbs. Also steam your peas for 2–4 minutes (or you can add them raw if you are using fresh).

Toast the pine nuts in a dry frying pan set over a low–medium heat for 5–7 minutes, until golden. Watch them closely – I burn them half the time doing too many things at once!

Let the pine nuts and the buckwheat cool, then mix with all the veggies and herbs. Squeeze over the lemon juice, drizzle with olive oil, add a pinch of salt and pepper, and mix everything together. Let it sit for at least 15 minutes before serving.

curried wild rice salad

This salad is one I make on a prep day and take to work for lunch throughout the week; it seems to taste better as the days go on. If you like a lot of heat use hot curry powder but if you just want a subtle hint go with mild.

serves 4 as a main, or 6 as a side

250g wild rice, washed
  and drained
750ml vegetable stock
juice of 1 lemon
4 tbsp extra virgin
  olive oil
1 tbsp raw honey
2 tsp wholegrain mustard
2 tsp curry powder (mild,
  medium or hot)
1 tsp ground cumin
½ tsp ground cinnamon
¼ tsp cayenne pepper
2 medium carrots, peeled
  and finely chopped
1 large red pepper, finely
  chopped
50g black olives, sliced
2 shallots, finely chopped
60g raisins, dried
  cranberries or dried
  cherries
60g roasted pecans (use
  my Spiced pecans
  recipe on page 218)
20g flat-leaf parsley,
  roughly chopped
salt and pepper

Cook the rice in the vegetable stock according to the packet instructions – it should take 45–55 minutes. Once cooked, drain and set aside.

Meanwhile, in a large mixing bowl, whisk together the lemon juice, olive oil, honey, mustard, curry powder, cumin, cinnamon and cayenne pepper.

Stir in the cooked and drained wild rice, then the carrots, red pepper, olives, shallots and raisins, cranberries or cherries. Season to taste with salt and pepper.

For the best flavour, chill in the refrigerator for at least 2 hours, and up to overnight, so as to allow the flavours to meld. When you are ready to serve, stir in half of the pecans and parsley, then sprinkle the other half on the top.

halloumi and lentil mediterranean salad

This might just be my perfect lunch. Completely balanced and nutritious, it will load you up with energy for the rest of the day. I often make a big batch of this when I have guests over at the weekend and then save enough so I can eat it for my lunch on Monday and Tuesday. You can always grill more cheese if you have excess lentil salad. (Photograph on page 45.)

serves 4

200g Puy lentils
1 litre vegetable stock
1 garlic clove, crushed
1 bay leaf
2 medium carrots,
  peeled and finely
  chopped
2 red peppers, finely
  chopped
2 shallots, finely
  chopped
a few sprigs flat-leaf
  parsley, roughly
  chopped
a few sprigs coriander,
  roughly chopped
1 x 250g block of
  halloumi, sliced into
  8 pieces

Place the Puy lentils, vegetable stock, garlic and bay leaf in a medium saucepan and cook for about 25–30 minutes on a medium heat, or until the lentils are tender but still holding their shape and retaining a little bite. Discard the bay leaf at the end of cooking.

Once cooked, run the lentils under cold water and drain, then place in a large serving bowl and mix with the carrot, red pepper, shallot, parsley and coriander.

Heat a large frying pan or griddle pan over a medium–high heat and cook the halloumi for 2–3 minutes on each side, or until golden brown.

Mix everything together and then, voilà! I like drizzling over a home-made dressing, such as my Great green tahini sauce (see page 247) for added flavour.

my mom's tempeh chilli

This recipe is a twist on the original chilli con carne, but using plant power instead of animal protein. My mom has mastered the art of seasoning – she adds just enough spice but never too much. If you really like a spicy kick, just add more cayenne. I serve my chilli over brown rice and top it with diced tomatoes and avocado for a cooling, fresh contrast to the spice.

serves 4

5 large vine tomatoes, quartered

2 tbsp extra virgin olive oil

2 small leeks (white part only), finely chopped

2 garlic cloves, finely chopped

1 yellow onion, finely chopped

200g tempeh, cut into 1cm cubes

1 x 400g can chopped tomatoes

1 x 400g can black beans, drained and rinsed

1 x 400g can kidney beans, drained and rinsed

1 tsp ground cinnamon

½ tsp cayenne pepper (optional)

½ tsp ground cumin

salt and pepper

1 avocado, sliced, to serve

lime wedges, to serve

2 tbsp finely chopped coriander, to serve

Preheat the oven to 180°C/gas 4. Place your vine tomatoes in a roasting tray, drizzle with a tablespoon of olive oil and season with salt and pepper. Roast for 30 minutes or until the edges of the tomatoes begin to darken.

Meanwhile, sauté the leeks, garlic, onion and tempeh in a tablespoon of olive oil over a medium heat until they begin to turn golden, about 7–8 minutes.

Add the chopped tomatoes and simmer on a low heat for another 15 minutes. Add a splash of water if the bottom of the pan begins to catch. Add the beans and roasted tomatoes.

Season with cinnamon, cayenne (if using), cumin, salt and pepper, then add 125ml water and simmer all together, covered with a lid, for another 30 minutes. Stir occasionally and add more water as needed if the mixture gets too thick.

Taste again to check for seasoning and serve with the avocado, lime wedges and coriander.

roasted root, spiced pecan and quinoa salad

You'll know by now that I'm a huge fan of quinoa. Any 'good grain' (or 'pseudo-grain' in this case) that is this tasty, versatile and contains protein is a winner in my book. This is one of my favourite quinoa salad recipes to make for Sunday lunch with friends or a dinner when I'm expecting a large group (as it's easy to double or triple this recipe). For extra-gorgeous presentation, use both yellow and red beetroot if you can source them.

serves 4 as a light lunch, or 6–8 as a side

For the salad:
500ml vegetable stock or water
200g uncooked white or red quinoa, rinsed
2 tsp cumin
3 large raw beetroot, scrubbed but not peeled, chopped into 2cm chunks
1 medium butternut squash, chopped into 2cm chunks
drizzle of olive oil
2 tsp dried rosemary
100g Spiced pecans (see page 218)
20 mint leaves, roughly chopped
salt and pepper

For the lemon vinaigrette:
½ tsp lemon zest, finely grated
2 tbsp fresh lemon juice
½ tsp Dijon mustard
3–4 tbsp extra virgin olive oil
salt and pepper

Preheat the oven to 180°C/gas 4. In a medium-sized saucepan, add the vegetable stock or water, quinoa and cumin and cook as per the packet instructions – it should take 12–15 minutes.

Pop the beetroot and butternut squash on a baking sheet and drizzle both with olive oil, then add salt and pepper and the dried rosemary. Place in the oven for 30–40 minutes, until cooked through but not mushy.

While the root vegetables are cooking, whisk together all of the ingredients for the lemon vinaigrette in a bowl and pop in the fridge until ready to pour.

Once the quinoa and vegetables are cooked, let each cool for 10 minutes.

In a large bowl, mix together the quinoa and vegetables with 50g of spiced pecans and the mint leaves.

Drizzle on the lemon vinaigrette and toss everything together. Top with the remaining pecans and serve.

herb and baked tofu summer rolls

This is one of those wonderful recipes that looks elaborate and fancy but is in fact really easy to make. All you need to find is a good place for buying rice paper rounds – either at a health-food shop, an Asian supermarket or online – and then you are ready to roll.

Although I've written this as a recipe, you should really just see this as a set of guidelines because you can roll up whatever you like. With the right dipping sauce, these rolls always taste delicious. This is my favourite combination, but there's no magic to what I have chosen. Other ingredients to play around with include cucumber, pineapple, beansprouts, green apple, grapefruit, fennel and ginger. Be adventurous . . .

makes 12 rolls

1 x quantity Tamari
   baked tofu (see
   page 211)
½ head (350g prepared
   weight) white Chinese
   cabbage, grated or
   thinly sliced
¼ head (150g prepared
   weight) purple
   cabbage, grated or
   thinly sliced
1 medium carrot, peeled
   and grated
15g coriander leaves,
   roughly chopped
10g mint leaves, roughly
   chopped
10g basil leaves, roughly
   chopped
juice of 1 lime
12 rice paper rounds
No-sugar peanut sauce
   (page 247), to serve

Cut the tofu slices into small cubes, then put all the vegetables and herbs together with the tofu in a mixing bowl. Squeeze the lime juice over the top and mix well.

Then comes the fun part – the assembly. Use a shallow bowl (a quiche dish works well) of warm water to soak your rice paper rounds, one at a time, until they are malleable. Then transfer the rice paper to a chopping board, lay flat and gently pat dry with kitchen paper.

Take small handfuls of your vegetable, herb and baked tofu mix and place in the middle of each round. Fold and roll up tightly, then repeat. Serve with the no-sugar peanut sauce alongside.

pesto portobello mushrooms

When I talk about making vegetables the centrepiece of your plate, this is exactly the sort of thing I'm referring to. These meaty mushrooms look spectacularly beautiful and are super-filling, making them a great main to impress guests, even if you're not cooking for vegetarians. You can serve them with a mixed leaf or tomato salad topped with one of my dressings (see pages 247–9).

serves 4

4 large Portobello
  mushrooms
2 tbsp extra virgin
  olive oil, plus extra
  for brushing
1 medium yellow onion,
  roughly chopped
1 garlic clove, finely
  sliced
juice of 1 lemon
4 tbsp Basil pesto (see
  page 241)
25g dried breadcrumbs
  (use gluten-free if
  possible), plus extra
  for topping (optional)
75g feta cheese,
  crumbled
½ tsp red chilli flakes
2–3 tbsp finely grated
  Parmesan
salt and pepper

Preheat the oven to 180°C/gas 4.

Brush the mushrooms to remove any dirt, then cut off the stalks. Set the mushroom tops aside and chop the stalks.

Heat the olive oil in a pan and add the chopped mushroom stalks, onion and garlic. Cook for 5–10 minutes, until soft. Then add the lemon juice, pesto, breadcrumbs, feta, chilli flakes and seasoning. Stir together until fully combined and heated.

Put everything in a blender or food processor and whizz until smooth. Brush a roasting dish and the Portobello mushrooms with a bit of olive oil, then place them on the dish, indented side up (so they are like little bowls). Fill each one with an equal amount of the pesto and feta mixture.

Top with grated Parmesan and breadcrumbs if you have any leftover (although this is not necessary). Bake for 25–30 minutes, until the top is slightly browned but not burned.

spiced chickpea, brown rice and veggie soup

For me there is nothing quite as satisfying (especially on cold winter days) as a warm, hearty soup that is teeming with nutritionally dense ingredients to boost your immune system. This one is also a great choice to make on a prep day when you can pick up lots of fresh vegetables and herbs.

serves 4

1 large onion, finely
  chopped
1–2 tbsp extra virgin
  olive oil
2 medium carrots, finely
  chopped
1 celery stick, finely
  chopped
½ medium fennel bulb,
  core removed, finely
  chopped
3 garlic cloves, finely
  chopped
1 litre vegetable stock
2 tsp cumin
1 tsp garam masala
1 tsp pepper
1 bay leaf
100g brown rice
2 handfuls (about 15)
  cherry tomatoes
1 x 400g can chickpeas,
  drained
2 tbsp roughly chopped
  flat-leaf parsley,
  to serve

In a large pot, sauté the onion in the olive oil over a medium heat for about 10 minutes or until it is soft. Add the carrots, celery and fennel, lower the heat and continue to cook, stirring, until they are also tender, about 8–10 minutes. If necessary, add a little more oil to the pan to prevent the vegetables catching.

Add the garlic and sauté until it starts to turn golden, around 2–3 minutes.

Add the stock and turn the heat to high for a few minutes, then bring the broth to a simmer and add the spices, pepper, bay leaf and brown rice. Cook uncovered for 10 minutes.

Add the tomatoes and chickpeas and simmer uncovered for another 35 minutes. Remove the bay leaf and add more pepper to taste. Top with a scattering of parsley before serving.

TLAT *(tempeh, lettuce, avocado and tomato)* sandwich

This is my version of the classic BLT (bacon, lettuce and tomato) sandwich. There is something about this plant-rich combination of savoury marinated tempeh along with crisp lettuce, tomato and buttery rich avocado that makes this the ultimate blend. Find the best wholegrain or gluten-free bread you can; the seedier the better – it makes all the difference. We make this for brunch, lunch or dinner; when I was pregnant I would dream about it for breakfast. (Vegetarians please note that Worcestershire sauce contains anchovies.)

serves 4

For the tempeh:
3–4 garlic cloves, peeled but left whole, or to taste
1–2 tbsp toasted sesame oil (or extra virgin olive oil if not available)
¼ large yellow onion, finely chopped
1 tsp mustard seeds
¼ tsp pepper
200g tempeh, cut into ½cm slices (about 12 slices)
2 tsp Worcestershire sauce
2 tbsp tamari
juice of 2 lemons

To assemble the sandwich:
8 slices of bread
mayonnaise (I use vegan mayonnaise)
wholegrain mustard
lettuce
avocado, sliced
tomatoes, sliced

In a sauté pan over a low–medium heat, heat the garlic cloves and 1 tablespoon of the sesame oil for about 5 minutes, until the garlic is browned. Then add the onion, mustard seeds and pepper and continue to cook over a gentle heat for 10 minutes or until the onion is soft and transparent.

Add the sliced tempeh, Worcestershire sauce, tamari and lemon juice to the pan. Allow everything to simmer until the liquid has reduced to a thick oniony paste. Lift out the tempeh and mash the garlic with a fork to break it down, then remove as much of the paste as you can from the pan with a spoon and save it to use as a delicious condiment for your sandwiches.

Add another tablespoon of oil if your pan is now dry, return the tempeh to the pan and continue to cook the strips for another 10 minutes, until most of the moisture has been removed and they become darker in colour. They will begin to look a bit like cooked bacon (a much better bacon!).

Toast the bread lightly and then slather a slice with mayonnaise and mustard. Add some tempeh strips along with a stack of lettuce, avocado and tomato slices, then top with some of the onion paste and a second slice of bread.

Keep your egg-fried rice real with this healthy, plant-packed alternative to a Chinese meal. This has got all the moreishness of a takeaway and is the perfect recipe to try when you need a super-quick dinner – especially if you cooked brown rice on your prep day or have leftovers from the day before. You can make the rice fresh, but it actually tastes better with leftover rice. This recipe is one to be creative with since you can mix in pretty much anything you like; I use different vegetables depending on what we have in the house and what's in season.

serves 4–6

800g leftover cooked brown rice or 275g uncooked brown rice

2 tbsp extra virgin olive oil (or sesame oil if you prefer the taste)

2 tbsp tamari

1 carrot, peeled and finely chopped

100g garden peas (frozen or fresh)

1 red pepper, finely chopped

½ courgette, finely chopped

2 garlic cloves, finely chopped

2.5cm ginger, peeled and grated

4 large eggs

juice of 1 lime

25g coriander or Thai basil leaves, finely chopped

If you aren't using leftover rice, cook your rice as per the packet instructions and when it's done cool it down under cold water and leave for a few minutes.

Heat the oil and tamari in a large sauté pan or wok over a medium heat. When hot, add all the veggies plus the garlic and ginger. Sauté until slightly softened, about 2–3 minutes. Then add the rice and stir together until the rice is heated through.

In a separate bowl, whisk your egg, then slowly add them to the pan, stirring all the while. You want the egg to cook a little bit at a time as it is being folded into the rice mixture.

Squeeze the lime juice into the pan and mix in the coriander or Thai basil before serving.

kale and tofu enchiladas

I grew up on the west coast of America, which meant we often treated ourselves to Mexican food and my mom was always creating healthy versions of the traditional dishes. Here I've tried to do the same. Mexican-inspired but Calgary-tweaked, this takes me back to my roots and like my mom's, has a bounty of nutrients rolled up inside each tortilla. These are equally great as a family dinner or a 'fancier' meal for friends and I love the leftovers cold for lunch the next day.

serves 4

For the tomato sauce:

2 x 400g cans chopped
   tomatoes
500g cherry tomatoes
1 garlic clove, chopped
1 tbsp extra virgin
   olive oil
1 tsp dried thyme
2 tsp dried basil (or 1
   handful of torn leaves)
salt and pepper

For the enchiladas:

1 tbsp extra virgin
   olive oil
2 small onions, roughly
   chopped
2 x 350g blocks firm
   tofu, drained and
   squeezed to remove
   excess water
100g kale, stalks
   removed, chopped
   into 1.5cm pieces
125g Cheddar cheese,
   grated
8 medium corn tortillas
200g salsa (mild or hot),
   to serve
My little sister's epic
   guacamole (see page
   245), to serve

Preheat the oven to 180°C/gas 4, then start by making your sauce. Put the chopped tomatoes in a saucepan, bring to the boil, then cook over a low heat for 45 minutes or until it has reduced. You are making a concentrated tomato base for your sauce – it brings out the flavour so much more.

Meanwhile, place the cherry tomatoes in a roasting dish with the garlic and drizzle with the olive oil. Roast in the oven for 25–30 minutes, until soft.

While the tomatoes are cooking, start to make the enchiladas. Heat the olive oil in a frying pan, add the onions and fry gently over a medium heat, until soft and translucent.

Crumble the tofu into the onion pan and fry gently over a medium heat until golden and the excess moisture has evaporated – about 30 minutes. You don't want to burn the tofu, which will happen if you try to rush this step. Patience is key! Now, add the kale and simmer until wilted, about 4–5 minutes. Let this mixture cool, then add half the cheese. Mix and season well.

Lay your tortillas flat on the kitchen surface or on a plate, and spoon 2 tablespoons of the tofu/kale mixture into the centre of each tortilla. Then wrap them up. Lay the rolled enchiladas in a 23 x 33cm baking dish.

Once both your tinned tomatoes and roasted cherry tomatoes are cooked, blitz both types of tomato and the roasted garlic with a hand blender. Check for seasoning, then return to the pan with the thyme and basil and cook for another 10 minutes. Now pour this tomato sauce over your rolled enchiladas and sprinkle the remaining cheese over the top.

Bake for 35–40 minutes or until bubbling and the cheese is golden. Serve with the salsa and guacamole.

feta, quinoa and pine nut stuffed courgettes

My Italian genes come to the fore in this recipe that my grandmother introduced me to decades ago. I have given it a healthy twist by swapping the couscous or rice for quinoa and adding beans for extra plant power, but the same great flavours remain. It makes a hearty supper served with green beans tossed in a light vinaigrette or a tomato and basil salad. And it's also great cold the next day, so don't be shy about having one for breakfast or packing some up in your 'lunch box'.

serves 6

100g quinoa, rinsed

6 large courgettes

1 x 400g can cannellini beans, drained, rinsed and roughly chopped

1 medium yellow onion, finely chopped

2 garlic cloves, crushed

2 tbsp flat-leaf parsley leaves, roughly chopped

1 tbsp mint leaves, finely chopped

125g crumbly feta or goats' cheese, chopped or crumbled

30g pine nuts, toasted

4 tbsp extra virgin olive oil

4 tbsp finely grated Parmesan

Preheat the oven to 200°C/gas 6. In a large saucepan over a high heat, combine the quinoa with 250ml water and bring to a boil. Reduce the heat to medium–low, cover and let simmer until the quinoa is tender and the water is absorbed, about 15 minutes.

While this is cooking, cut the courgettes in half lengthwise and scoop out the seeds and some of the flesh – this pulp can be discarded or used as part of a vegetable stock. Arrange in a large baking dish, cut-side up.

When the quinoa is done, fluff it with a fork, then add the beans, onion, garlic, herbs, feta or goats' cheese, toasted pine nuts and 3 tablespoons of the olive oil.

Mix that all up roughly with a fork, then spoon the mixture into the courgette boats. Top with the remaining 1 tablespoon of oil and the grated Parmesan.

Cover with foil and bake until the courgettes are tender; this will take 20–30 minutes, depending on their size. Once tender, remove the foil and bake for 10–15 minutes or until the top is golden brown.

sweet potato, kale and chickpea coconut curry

A bowl of this hearty, aromatic stew is guaranteed to warm the soul. It's intensely flavoured, creamy and filling – qualities that I think make the best one-bowl meals. If you're not vegetarian, don't skip the fish sauce – it adds a fantastic depth of flavour. This is great served with brown rice, quinoa or millet. I always bring my leftovers to work the next day and the whole office is jealous of the coconut curry fragrances wafting from my desk. (Photograph on page 86.)

serves 6

1 x 400ml can coconut
  milk
200ml vegetable stock
  or water
5cm ginger, peeled and
  finely chopped
2 lemongrass stalks,
  bruised slightly to
  release flavour
2 medium sweet
  potatoes (350g
  prepared weight),
  peeled and cut into
  1.5cm cubes
2 x 400g cans chickpeas,
  drained and rinsed
1 tbsp extra virgin
  olive oil
50g kale, stalks
  removed, roughly
  chopped
juice of 1 lime
1 tbsp fish sauce
  (optional)
2 tsp roughly chopped
  basil leaves (sweet
  Thai basil if you can
  find it)
salt

In a large pan, simmer the coconut milk, vegetable stock, ginger and lemongrass for 15 minutes to infuse the flavours. Then add the sweet potato and chickpeas, cover with a lid and leave to simmer while you cook the kale.

Heat the olive oil in a sauté pan over a low–medium heat, add the chopped kale and cook, stirring, until it begins to wilt. Then turn down to a very low heat and cook for about 10 minutes, until tender.

Remove the kale from the pan, drain off any excess water, then add to your coconut/sweet potato mixture. Cook all together for another 15 minutes; the sweet potato should now be tender. Remove the lemongrass stems.

Taste for seasoning – it may need a little salt – and stir through the lime juice, fish sauce, if using, and the basil.

Risotto is one of my ultimate comfort foods but I'm always on a mission to make it more nutritious and plant-based than your average bowl of white Arborio rice. This dish is bursting with rich flavours. Using buckwheat in place of the rice not only adds a delicious nutty complement to the earthy mushrooms but it means your risotto is powering you up with loads of nutrients. The recipe is best when you use an interesting mix of mushrooms to give it complexity, however I have made it with just one variety and it still tastes delicious.

serves 4–6

2 tbsp unsalted butter

2 tbsp extra virgin olive oil

300g mushrooms (try a combination), sliced

2 leeks, halved lengthwise and sliced into half circles

1 garlic clove, finely chopped

4 shallots, finely chopped

1 tsp thyme leaves, finely chopped, or ½ tsp dried thyme

300g raw buckwheat groats

750ml–1 litre vegetable stock

salt and pepper

a few leaves of flat-leaf parsley, to garnish

For the hazelnut cream:

70g hazelnuts, soaked in water overnight (or as long as you can), then rinsed

250ml water

Heat 1 tablespoon of butter and 1 tablespoon of olive oil in a sauté pan over a medium heat. Once they are melted together, add the sliced mushrooms and a pinch of salt. Stir and coat the mushrooms and continue to let this cook for 10 minutes or until the mushrooms are tender and beginning to turn golden. Remove from the heat.

In another deep sauté pan, heat the other tablespoon of butter and olive oil over a medium heat and add the leeks, garlic, shallots and thyme. Cook for 10 minutes, stirring occasionally, until everything is softened and starting to become golden.

Rinse the buckwheat groats, then add them to the leek mixture and allow them to 'toast' for a few minutes with all these flavours. Once infused, add the vegetable stock, 120ml at a time, stirring frequently and keeping the mixture at a simmer. Keep adding the stock until the buckwheat is tender, usually 20–30 minutes, but this will vary depending on the type of buckwheat and how long you've had it in your cupboard.

In the meantime make your hazelnut cream. Place all the ingredients in a food processor or blender and whizz until completely smooth.

Turn off the heat, add the mushrooms and hazelnut cream to the buckwheat and stir to combine. Add salt and pepper to taste and garnish with parsley.

black bean burgers

'Burger night' at our house is always a highly anticipated meal – it's guaranteed fun to stack your own with lots of favourite toppings to make it bespoke. I am always trying new vegetarian burger recipes but this is one of my family's top choices and we make it over and over again. Try serving these with a fresh spinach salad, topped with toasted pine nuts and chopped apple.

makes 4 burgers

225g cooked black
  beans or 1 x 400g can
  black beans, drained
  and rinsed
1 garlic clove, chopped
½ yellow onion, roughly
  chopped
juice of ½ lemon
1 medium egg yolk,
  beaten
25g flat-leaf parsley,
  finely chopped
25g Parmesan, finely
  grated
40g toasted
  breadcrumbs (use
  gluten-free if possible)
2 tsp Dijon mustard
½ tsp salt
½ tsp pepper
1 tbsp cumin

Preheat the oven to 190°C/gas 5. Line a baking sheet with baking parchment. Pour half of the black beans plus the garlic, onion and lemon juice into a food processor. Pulse until smooth.

Place the mixture in a mixing bowl and add the other half of the black beans and all of the other ingredients. Mix together so that everything is incorporated and well combined.

Divide the mixture into four and shape into burgers. Place in the fridge for 15–30 minutes on the prepared baking sheet to firm up. Bake in the oven for 15–20 minutes, until they are cooked through.

baked sweet potato boats with tasty toppings

Sweet potatoes are a great easy base for a meal, so they are a real go-to for me. The recipe below should simply serve as inspiration for you to make it your own. Play around with what you put on top, but just try to keep it plant-based and healthy – a sweet potato topped with loads of butter and bacon isn't exactly what I have in mind!

serves 2

2 medium sweet
  potatoes
1 tbsp extra virgin
  olive oil
Himalayan or sea salt

Heat your oven to 200°C/gas 6. Scrub your potatoes and pop them in a baking dish. Rub the oil all over the potatoes, then sprinkle with sea salt. Cover with foil and bake for 30 minutes, then remove the foil and leave for a further 15 minutes, until the flesh is cooked through and the skin is crispy.

MEXICAN BOATS

175g fresh corn kernels, cut from the cob,
  or tinned sweetcorn, rinsed
½ x 400g can black beans, drained and
  rinsed
6 heaped tbsp My little sister's epic
  guacamole (see page 245)
½ lime
4 coriander stalks, roughly chopped

If you are using fresh corn, cook the loose kernels in a pan of boiling water for 2–3 minutes.

Slice your baked sweet potatoes open, then top with the corn, beans and guacamole, then add a squeeze of lime juice and sprinkle over the coriander.

MEDITERRANEAN BOATS

60g feta cheese, crumbled
1 red chilli, deseeded and finely chopped
  (add less if you don't want it spicy)
2 tbsp extra virgin olive oil
30g pitted black olives
4 coriander stalks, chopped
25g pumpkin seeds
½ lime, for squeezing

Mix the feta, chilli, olive oil, olives and coriander in a bowl. Leave to sit for 1 hour if possible or as long as you can.

In a small frying pan set over a medium heat, toast the pumpkin seeds for about 7 minutes, until they start to turn golden.

Once your potatoes are ready, leave them to cool slightly, then slice them open, top with a few spoonfuls of the feta mixture, scatter over the toasted pumpkin seeds and squeeze some lime juice over the top.

vegan lasagne

I love the comfort of baked pasta dishes so I wanted to create a lasagne that was oozing with plant-based goodness but still made me feel all fuzzy inside. If you aren't vegan, you can add shredded mozzarella and grated Parmesan to each layer.

serves 8

For the tofu sauce:
4 tbsp olive oil
1 onion, roughly chopped
1 carrot, finely chopped
1 celery stick, finely chopped
3 garlic cloves, finely chopped
4 x 400g cans chopped tomatoes
5 tbsp tomato purée
2 bay leaves
700g firm tofu
pinch of cayenne pepper
1 large handful of basil leaves, chopped
1 large handful of flat-leaf parsley, chopped
salt and pepper

For the lasagne:
3 large courgettes
2 tbsp olive oil
800g fresh spinach (or frozen, thawed and drained)
½ tsp freshly grated nutmeg
200g dried, no pre-cook lasagne sheets
200g mozzarella and/or Parmesan (optional)

To make the sauce, heat 3 tablespoons of olive oil in a large saucepan over a medium heat, then add the chopped onion, carrot, celery and garlic and sauté for around 10 minutes or until soft. Then add the tomatoes, tomato purée and bay leaves. Stir well, turn the heat to low and let the sauce simmer, covered, for 1 hour.

Meanwhile, pat the tofu with kitchen roll to remove excess moisture. Heat the remaining tablespoon of oil in a large frying pan over a medium heat and then crumble in the tofu. Cook for 5–7 minutes, until the excess water from the tofu has evaporated and the tofu and the pan appear dry. Stir in the cayenne pepper and remove from the heat.

Once the tomato sauce has cooked and reduced, remove from the heat and stir in the tofu. Stir well to combine and leave the tofu to infuse in the tomato sauce while you prepare the courgettes.

Cut each courgette lengthwise into 0.5cm slices. Heat a griddle pan over a medium heat, lightly brush the courgette slices with the oil and griddle them in batches so you achieve nice char marks and the courgettes are tender. As they cook, remove them to a large plate. Season lightly with salt and pepper and repeat to cook the remainder. ➤

If you are using fresh spinach, place half in a large colander, sit the colander in the sink and boil a kettle of water. Pour the boiling water over the spinach; this will cook the spinach so it wilts. Refresh with cold water, then squeeze out the excess water and place in a sieve while you repeat with the remaining spinach. Once all cooked, give it a final squeeze to extract any excess water still remaining, then place on a chopping board and chop well. Season with salt and nutmeg.

Preheat the oven to 180°C/gas 4. Remove the bay leaves from your tomato sauce and add the chopped basil and parsley. Season to taste.

To assemble the lasagne, spread one ladle of the tomato sauce in the bottom of a 23 x 33cm baking dish. Arrange a single layer of lasagne sheets on top, followed by a third of the wilted spinach and then a third of courgette, then sprinkle with cheese (if using). Then add another layer of sauce and repeat the process two more times so your lasagne has three layers of pasta sheets and finishes with a layer of sauce and (if using) is topped with cheese.

Cover the lasagne with aluminium foil and bake in the oven for 25–30 minutes or until the pasta sheets are cooked. If you have added cheese to the top of your lasagne, remove the foil and cook for a further 10–15 minutes or until the cheese has begun to turn golden.

Remove from the oven and allow to cool for 15 minutes before serving. If you are freezing, let it cool completely and then place in the freezer in individually wrapped portion sizes.

tasty almond snacks, *two ways*

I can't imagine a day without eating a handful of almonds as a snack, and as much as I love almonds completely plain and raw, I'm always keen to find great flavour combinations in which to roast them. This zesty lemon is one of my best – it's mildly sweet from the coconut with a bite of sour from the lemon. And the first time I tried almonds flavoured with tamari I was hooked. Yet for years I bought them in health-food shops – my pocket taking a hit for something that, as it turns out, is actually really easy to make at home. I have worked with lots of different ingredient combinations in my quest to find the best one, but I think I've finally found the winner.

ZESTY LEMON COCONUT ALMONDS
serves 4–6

250g plain whole almonds (not roasted,
    salted or sweetened), soaked in water
    overnight (or as long as you can), then
    drained and rinsed
1 tbsp melted coconut oil
juice of 1 lemon
1 tsp salt
½ tsp ground black pepper

Preheat the oven to 180°C/gas 4 and line a baking sheet with baking parchment.

In a large mixing bowl, combine the drained almonds, coconut oil, lemon juice, salt and pepper.

Mix everything together thoroughly with your hands. Pick the almonds up, leaving the liquid in the bowl, and lay flat on the baking sheet.

Roast in the oven for 10–15 minutes or until dried and golden, stirring them a few times so that they cook evenly. Leave to cool. Store in an airtight container – they will stay fresh for up to 5 days.

TAMARI ALMONDS
serves 4–6

250g plain whole almonds (not roasted,
    salted or sweetened), soaked in water
    overnight (or as long as you can), then
    drained and rinsed
drizzle of extra virgin olive oil
1 tbsp tamari
1 tsp maple syrup
1 tsp chilli powder
1 tsp paprika
1 tsp ground turmeric
salt and pepper

Preheat the oven to 180°C/gas 4 and line a baking sheet with baking parchment.

Put the almonds into a bowl and toss with enough olive oil to coat. Stir through the tamari and maple syrup. Sprinkle over the chilli powder, paprika and turmeric and some salt and pepper and mix well.

Drain off any excess liquid and spread the nuts out on the baking sheet. Roast in the oven for 10–15 minutes or until beginning to turn golden, stirring them a few times so that they cook evenly. Leave to cool then store as for the zesty lemon almonds.

sunshine sunflower balls

Who couldn't like something called a sunshine ball? Fast to make and easy to transport as snacks, these are great to whip out whenever you find yourself in need of a healthy boost of energy. They are also very low in sugar, which makes them an extra good choice. Many energy balls are made with dates but these are not so they taste super satisfying without being overly sweet.

makes 15

25g cacao powder

35g chia seeds

75g sunflower seeds

45g desiccated coconut (unsweetened), plus extra for coating

70g jumbo oats (gluten-free if possible)

4 tbsp coconut milk (unsweetened; from a carton)

160g almond butter

2½ tbsp coconut oil, melted

1 tsp vanilla extract

Put all the dry ingredients into a blender or food processor and mix together. Then add in the rest of the ingredients and whizz everything until smooth.

Roll the mixture into small balls in the palm of your hand, and then roll each in desiccated coconut for a coating.

Put the balls on a baking sheet in the fridge to set for 1 hour. Store them either in an airtight container in the fridge. They will keep for 5–7 days.

matcha cacao macaroons

These are going to be your new go-to treats, I promise. With no refined sugar, you'll soon be replacing your afternoon chocolate fix with one of these coconut chocolate nuggets. They have the added benefit of a matcha kick to boost your energy and improve your concentration and are terribly easy to make, so get mixing! (Photograph on p91)

makes about 10

110g fresh coconut
  meat, finely grated
4 tbsp coconut oil,
  softened
3 tbsp cacao powder,
  plus an extra 1–2 tbsp
  for dusting
3 tbsp maple syrup
¼ tsp bee pollen
  (optional)
1 tbsp matcha powder
½ tsp vanilla extract
1 tbsp flaxseeds
desiccated coconut
  (unsweetened), for
  rolling

Throw all the ingredients together in a mixing bowl and mix together thoroughly. Use your hands to roll into balls and then cool in the fridge for 1–2 hours.

You can dust the outside of your macaroons with extra cacao if desired; simply remove after 30 minutes of chilling time, place the extra cacao on a plate and roll the macaroons until evenly coated. Return to the fridge to set.

Store in an airtight container in the fridge so they retain their shape – they will keep for 5–7 days.

banana, pecan and cacao nib muffins

These fruity muffins have the crunch of pecan nuts and cacao nibs (think of them as healthy chocolate chips) and make great breakfasts, after-school snacks or even desserts. Buckwheat flour has a very distinctive nutty flavour and is gluten-free, but if you aren't trying to be gluten-free all of the time you can use half wholemeal flour and half buckwheat flour.

makes 10 muffins

150g buckwheat flour
¾ tsp bicarbonate of soda
1 tbsp chia seeds
3 ripe medium bananas, mashed
2 tbsp coconut oil, melted
¼ tsp Himalayan or sea salt
1 tbsp fresh lemon juice
125ml almond milk (unsweetened)
1 vanilla pod, split and seeds scraped out
75g raw pecans, roughly chopped
25g cacao nibs

Preheat the oven to 150°C/gas 2. Line 10 holes of a muffin tin with muffin cases.

Sift the buckwheat flour and bicarbonate of soda together into a mixing bowl.

In another bowl, mix the chia seeds with 3 tablespoons of water, then add the mashed bananas, coconut oil, salt, lemon juice, almond milk and vanilla seeds and whisk together quickly to form a batter.

Fold the flour mix into the batter, then fold in the pecans and cacao nibs. Divide the batter between the muffin cases and bake for 20–25 minutes or until a skewer inserted into a muffin comes out clean.

Once cooled, the muffins can be kept in an airtight container at room temperature for up to 2 days.

coconut spirulina energy balls

These little power balls take no time at all to make and once you have a stocked pantry you'll have all the ingredients ready to go at any time. I often pop one in my mouth as a pre-exercise pick-me-up or offer them to my kids as an after-school snack. Remember, though, that they call for dates, which contain naturally-occurring sugar, so think of them as treats.

makes 10

45g hazelnuts
100g Medjool dates, pitted
45g desiccated coconut (unsweetened)
2 tbsp softened coconut oil
1 tbsp spirulina powder
2 tbsp raw cacao powder, plus extra for dusting

Line a baking sheet with baking parchment. Place the hazelnuts in a blender and blitz so they are finely ground but still have some texture, rather than being a paste.

Add the remaining ingredients to your blender and whizz together until combined.

Shape the mixture into balls by rolling in the palm of your hands, then lightly roll the balls in some cacao powder.

Pop in the fridge on the baking sheet for 30 minutes, until set. They will last for 1 week if kept refrigerated and stored in an airtight container.

chocolate, cranberry and buckwheat cookies

Everyone has a weakness and cookies are mine, so I felt compelled to include a killer recipe in my book. These are decadent but still contain lots of wholesome ingredients and don't taste overly sweet. I usually double the batch when I make them and freeze the extras. It's always nice to have cookies ready for a rainy day…

makes about 15

125g buckwheat flour
25g cacao powder
½ tsp Himalayan salt
½ tsp baking soda
120g dark chocolate
  (70 per cent cocoa
  solids), roughly
  chopped
150g coconut sugar
4 tbsp coconut oil,
  melted
2 medium eggs
1 tsp vanilla extract
80g dried cranberries
shelled hemp seeds,
  to sprinkle

Combine the buckwheat flour, cacao, salt and baking soda in a medium bowl and mix thoroughly. Set aside.

Put the chocolate in a small heatproof bowl and sit it above a pan of simmering water without letting the bottom of the bowl touch the water. Allow it to melt, stirring occasionally.

In a food processor, blend the coconut sugar with the coconut oil. Add the eggs one by one, then add the vanilla extract and finally the melted chocolate. Mix until just combined.

Add the chocolate mix to the dry ingredients and mix with a rubber spatula. Then fold in the dried cranberries and mix until combined.

Preheat the oven to 180°C/gas 4 and line a baking sheet with baking parchment.

Place the mixture in the fridge for 20 minutes to cool down. Once the dough has cooled a little, you are ready to bake.

Drop tablespoons of the sticky chocolate mix on the prepared baking sheet, leaving 5cm between each cookie, then sprinkle with hemp seeds.

Bake for 10 minutes, then remove from the oven and let them cool on the baking sheet for 5–8 minutes before transferring to a wire rack. The cookies will feel quite soft when they first come out of the oven but will firm up when they cool down.

Once cooled, the cookies can be kept in an airtight container at room temperature for up to 5 days.

chocolate brownies, *two ways*

Brownies are such a crowd pleaser that I wanted at least a couple of healthy versions in my book and what follows are two of the best I've ever tried. Roots & Bulbs is a fantastic destination for healthy food in London. They also spoil their customers with ridiculously good brownies and generously gave me their recipe so that I could offer you the same decadence. 'Made By Margie' is a wonderful blog written by Margie Broadhead and I fell so hard in love with her brownies that I wanted to share them too. I like to serve these for guests with a dollop of coconut yoghurt.

CHOCOLATE AND WALNUT BROWNIES BY *ROOTS & BULBS*

makes about 9

125g dried black beans, soaked overnight
2 large eggs
45g cacao powder
4 tbsp maple syrup
4 tsp raw clear honey
pinch of sea salt
1 vanilla pod, split and seeds scraped
125g coconut oil, melted
100g walnuts, roughly chopped

Drain the beans and cook in simmering water for 50 minutes, or until soft.

Preheat the oven to 160°C/gas 3 and line a 20 x 20cm baking tin with baking parchment. In a food processor, blend the beans with the eggs, cacao, maple syrup, honey, salt and vanilla seeds until smooth. Blend in the coconut oil and half of the walnuts.

Spoon the mixture into the tray and spinkle over the extra walnuts. Tap the tray to smooth out the mixture and remove any large air bubbles. Bake for 25–30 minutes or until the brownie is firm to the touch. Allow to cool completely before cutting and serving.

RASPBERRY AND COCONUT BROWNIES *BY MADE BY MARGIE*

makes about 9

260g dark chocolate (70 per cent cocoa
   solids), broken into small pieces
1 x 400g can black beans, rinsed and
   drained
25g cocoa powder (unsweetened)
2 medium eggs
3½ tbsp coconut oil, melted
¼ tsp ground cinnamon
1 tbsp vanilla extract
generous pinch of salt
½ tsp baking powder
1 tsp instant coffee
2 tbsp maple syrup
150g raspberries

Preheat the oven to 180°C/gas 4. Line a 20 x 20cm baking tin with parchment.

Pop everything except the raspberries into a food processor and blend until combined and creamy. Don't worry if there are still lumps of chocolate. Pour the batter into the tin and smooth it out, then tip the raspberries on top and push them down. Bake in the oven for 35 minutes, or until firm to the touch and a toothpick comes out clean-ish. Cool before cutting. into squares and devouring.

cashew thumbprint cookies

My kids are my most trusted recipe testers – I try everything on them first. Sometimes I get a 'that's okay' or 'that tastes weird', but these super-easy raw cookies got a 'Mummy, these are delicious! Can I have another?', so my bet is you'll like them too. All you need is a food processor and a refrigerator to make these tasty little bites.

Traditional 'thumbprint' cookies are topped with jam but these aren't exactly traditional! I personally like them left plain and just dusted with a bit of cinnamon or cacao powder, but you could also top them each with an individual raspberry, a blueberry, a whole cashew, a small chunk of dark chocolate or carob.

makes 15

100g plain cashews

3 tbsp coconut oil, softened

2–3 Medjool dates, pitted

2 tbsp plain sunflower seeds (not flavoured or roasted)

1 tsp vanilla extract

pinch of salt

75g rolled oats (gluten-free if possible)

Simply throw everything – except the oats – in a food processor and blend until it has the consistency of a thick paste. Scrape down the sides of the food processor a few times as needed. Then add the oats and pulse again until everything is blended together. If at this stage the mixture doesn't quite hold together sufficiently, add another date and pulse again.

With your hands, roll the dough into 15 small balls and place on a baking sheet. (I usually put baking parchment down on the baking sheet just to make cleaning up easier.) Push down the centre of each cookie with your thumb.

Place the sheet in the refrigerator for 2–6 hours, until firm, and keep them stored there afterwards in an airtight container. They will last for 7 days.

autumn spiced plums and cinnamon cashew cream

I love a high-impact, easy recipe. These warming, aromatic plums take hardly any time to prepare yet people are always wowed by the combination of flavours and the vibrancy of the colour. The nutty cream is a decadent yet wonderfully healthy accompaniment, but you can serve the plums with Greek yoghurt depending on what you have in the fridge. Any leftover cashew cream can be served over granola, sliced fruit, porridge or muesli for breakfast. I think just about anything tastes better with cinnamon cashew cream.

serves 8–10

For the spiced plums:
10 plums, halved and pitted
2 tbsp softened coconut oil
4 tbsp maple syrup
3 tsp ground cinnamon
2 star anise (optional)
3 tbsp balsamic vinegar
375ml water
60g shelled pistachios

For the cinnamon cashew cream:
125g plain cashews (not roasted, salted or sweetened), soaked in water overnight (or as long as you can – 1 hour minimum), then drained
125ml almond milk (unsweetened)
1 tbsp raw honey
½ tsp ground cinnamon
¼ tsp ground nutmeg

Preheat oven to 180°C/gas 4. Arrange the plums, cut-side up, in a baking dish that is large enough to hold the plums in one layer. Coat each plum with a thin layer of coconut oil using your hands.

In a medium-sized saucepan, combine the maple syrup, cinnamon, star anise (if using), balsamic vinegar and water, bringing the mixture to a boil.

Pour the sauce over the plums in the baking dish and cover with foil, then bake in the oven until tender, about 1 hour.

Meanwhile, make the cashew cream. Whizz everything together in a food processor or high-powered blender until completely smooth and creamy. Chill and store in the refrigerator until needed – it will keep for up to three days.

In a small frying pan on a low heat, toast the pistachios until they smell aromatic.

Remove the plums from the oven, lift off the foil and let them cool slightly. Sprinkle the plums with the pistachios and serve with the cashew cream.

gluten-free apricot and thyme tart

It's hard not to beam with pride when you serve this tart. It's a gorgeous way to end any meal and guests will undoubtedly be impressed. Nobody ever has to know this is far healthier than your average tart – it just shows that healthy truly can be decadent.

serves 8

For the crust:

2 tbsp coconut oil, melted, plus extra for oiling the tin
30g rolled oats (gluten-free if possible)
20g desiccated coconut (unsweetened)
95g gluten-free oat flour
¼ tsp Himalayan salt
105g ground almonds
40g millet or rice flour
75ml maple syrup
finely grated zest of 1 organic lemon
whipped coconut cream, to serve

For the filling:

35g ground almonds
20g coconut sugar
pinch of Himalayan salt
8 apricots, pitted and sliced 1cm thick
1½ tbsp coconut oil, melted
4 tsp maple syrup
1 tsp vanilla extract
finely grated zest of 1 organic lime
1 tsp thyme leaves
10g almond flakes

Preheat the oven to 180°C/gas 4 and oil a 22cm round or 36 x 13cm loose-bottomed tart tin.

To make the crust, place the rolled oats, desiccated coconut, oat flour and salt in a food processor and pulse until they are finely ground and resemble flour. Transfer to a bowl and add the ground almonds and the millet or rice flour. Stir in the coconut oil and mix with your hands until the flour is moistened. Add the maple syrup and lemon zest and mix until combined and you can form a ball – the dough should hold together. If it's too dry add 1 teaspoon of an unsweetened nut milk; if too sticky let it rest for 5–10 minutes, until it firms up.

Press the dough into the prepared tart tin, being sure to cover the base and sides. Trim any excess dough, then prick the base of the case all over with a fork. Bake for 12 minutes or until the pastry is just set but not cooked through. Remove from the oven and set aside.

To prepare the filling, in a bowl combine the ground almonds, coconut sugar and a pinch of salt. Set aside.

Place the apricot slices in a bowl together with the coconut oil, maple syrup, vanilla extract, lime zest and thyme. Gently mix, taking care not to mash the fruit.

To assemble, spread the ground almond/sugar mixture over the crust then arrange slices of apricots on top, overlapping them slightly. Sprinkle the almond flakes over the apricots.

Place the tart in the oven and bake for 25–30 minutes, until the crust is golden in colour and the apricots are soft. Remove from the oven and let cool slightly before serving with a thick dollop of whipped coconut cream.

frozen raw matcha cheesecake

This 'cheese' cake's deliciously creamy centre and rich crunchy crust make it one of my star treats and I look for any excuse to make it. It looks beautiful, making it a great choice to serve for guests and I've even made it as a birthday cake. It's best served directly from the fridge.

treats & desserts

serves 8

For the crust:
320g plain macadamia
  nuts (not roasted,
  salted or sweetened)
10g raw cacao powder
65g maple syrup
15g cacao nibs
1 tsp vanilla extract
½ tsp Himalayan salt

For the filling:
2 tbsp matcha
  powder, plus an extra
  ¼ tsp to decorate
2 ½ hot water, plus an
  extra ¼ tsp
470g plain cashews,
  soaked overnight or
  for as long as you can,
  then rinsed
435ml unsweetened nut
  milk (I use almond)
3 tbsp fresh lemon juice
2 tbsp fresh lime juice
190g raw agave syrup
1 tbsp vanilla extract
pinch of Himalayan salt
6 tbsp coconut oil,
  melted

To prepare the crust, line the base of a 22cm spring-form tin with baking parchment.

In a food processor blend the macadamia nuts with the cacao powder until it resembles flour; be careful not to overmix or you will end up with macadamia nut butter!

Remove from the food processor and combine in a bowl with the maple syrup, cacao nibs, vanilla and salt. Mix well and press the mixture into the spring-form tin to form the crust. Set aside.

To prepare the filling, mix the matcha with the hot water in a small bowl. Set aside.

In a high-speed blender, mix the cashews, nut milk, lemon and lime juice, agave syrup, vanilla extract and salt until smooth. Then add the matcha mix and blend again. With the blender running, add the coconut oil and blend until completely smooth.

In a small bowl mix the extra ¼ teaspoon of matcha with ¼ teaspoon of hot water. Set aside to decorate.

To assemble, pour the cheesecake filling on top of the crust. Carefully shake the mould to level the mixture and get rid of any air bubbles. Pour the extra matcha mixture on top of the filling and use the tip of a small knife to swirl it and create whatever design you like.

Cover with cling film and place in the freezer for 3 hours.

Remove the cheesecake from the freezer and carefully release it from the spring-form tin. Keep it in the fridge until serving.

vegan ice cream, *three ways*

These recipes were developed with my kids in mind. I wanted to treat them to ice cream that I felt good about serving them but that they felt happy eating. The use of nut butter in the mixture means they are remarkably rich and creamy – yet super healthy – so only the most die-hard dairy addicts are going to notice the lack of cream. These are mine and my kids' favourite flavour combinations but, as you can see, the basic recipe is so simple that it's really easy to play around and create your own combinations.

THE ORIGINAL

serves 2

2 bananas, broken into
  2.5cm-long pieces then
  frozen
1 tbsp peanut butter
  (unsweetened)
1 tsp ground cinnamon

Put the frozen banana into a blender or food processor with the peanut butter and cinnamon. Blend together until very creamy (it can take a while to get it really creamy), then pop into a bowl and leave in the freezer for a few hours until frozen. If frozen for longer than a couple of hours the ice cream becomes very solid, so allow to defrost a little before serving.

Hey presto! Fast, easy and incredibly delicious vegan ice cream.

CHOCOLATEY COCONUT VEGAN ICE CREAM

serves 2

2 bananas, broken into
  2.5cm-long pieces then
  frozen
2 tbsp almond butter
  (unsweetened)
2 tbsp desiccated coconut
  (unsweetened)
1 tbsp cacao powder

Whizz all together, freeze and serve.

BLUEBERRY AND MINT VEGAN ICE CREAM

serves 2

2 bananas, broken into
  2.5cm-long pieces then
  frozen
1 tbsp peanut butter
  (unsweetened)
1 tsp ground cinnamon
75g blueberries
30 mint leaves

Whizz all together, freeze and serve.

The great thing about popsicles (aka ice lollies) is that you can pretty much use any combination of fruit to create delicious treats that will instantly make you happy and leave you thinking of long summer days. The other great thing is that basically any smoothie you make can be poured into your moulds, so if you ever have any leftover you can freeze it into popsicles to save it for later.

These recipes are all just a guide as there are so many delicious choices available. Play around with whatever fruits and vegetables look gorgeous at your market. You can buy a variety of fun moulds so how many you can make depends on their size and shape – the quantities below all make six in my moulds.

450g strawberries, hulled

1 x 400ml can coconut milk

½ tbsp vanilla extract

Put everything in a blender or food processor, whizz and then freeze in popsicle moulds. They last well for up to 7 days.

1 large avocado, pitted and peeled

1 lime, peeled

250ml coconut water

1 tbsp matcha powder

Put everything in a blender or food processor, whizz and then freeze in popsicle moulds. They last well for up to 7 days.

1 large ripe mango, peeled and sliced
  into pieces

4 tbsp canned coconut milk

juice of ½ lime

1 tsp vanilla extract

6 basil leaves

a couple of pinches of toasted desiccated
  coconut (unsweetened)

Put everything in a blender or food processor, whizz and then freeze in popsicle moulds. They last well for up to 7 days.

250g plain Greek yoghurt

5 fresh ripe whole figs, stalks removed

50g soft mild goats' cheese

seeds of ½ scraped vanilla pod (or 1 tsp
  vanilla extract)

pinch of salt

Put everything in a blender or food processor, whizz and then freeze in popsicle moulds. They last well for up to 7 days.

pesto, *three ways*

My Italian roots influenced the fact that I had to give you three pesto recipes. The traditional basil version was simply a must. The spinach pesto has no cheese so it's a 100 per cent vegan option, perfect with pasta but also great as a dip for crudités or a spread on sandwiches. And for something a bit different, why not try a hemp seed pesto? You can use it in the same way as you would basil pesto and, although it doesn't taste drastically different, it does have a richer, nuttier flavour and is a bit more hearty and packed with protein. If you have any leftover pesto, freeze it in ice cube trays (see page 56).

BASIL PESTO

makes 200g

60g basil leaves
40g Parmesan, freshly
  grated
50g pine nuts
1–2 garlic cloves
125ml extra virgin olive oil
salt and pepper

Combine the basil, Parmesan, pine nuts and garlic in a food processor or blender. Pulse and then pick up the speed to get everything finely mixed. With the machine running, slowly add olive oil until you achieve your desired consistency. Add salt and pepper to taste.

SPINACH PESTO

makes 225g

100g baby spinach
15 basil leaves
125ml extra virgin olive oil
1 small garlic clove, finely
  chopped
90g pine nuts
½ tsp ground black pepper

Simply add all the ingredients to your blender or food processor and whizz together until smooth. Add more oil if necessary and if you like a stronger basil flavour, add extra leaves.

HEMP SEED PESTO

makes 125g

30g basil leaves
65g shelled hemp seeds
3 tbsp fresh lemon juice
2 garlic cloves
½ tsp freshly ground black
  pepper
½ tsp salt
100–125ml extra virgin
  olive oil
½ tsp red pepper flakes
  (optional)
3 tbsp freshly grated
  Parmesan (optional)

Simply add all the ingredients to your blender or food processor and whizz together until smooth. Add more oil if necessary.

sun-dried tomato and artichoke dip

I make this dip so frequently I can almost do it with my eyes closed. It's such a crowd-pleaser that I can't help myself but serve it over and over again. All those amazingly tasty ingredients blended together make something truly memorable – try it and you'll see what I mean!

makes 425g

1 x 390g can artichoke hearts (in water), drained then chopped
100g feta cheese
1 garlic clove, crushed
2 tsp fresh lemon juice
75g sun-dried tomatoes (in oil), chopped, plus extra for garnish
30g pine nuts, toasted
10g basil leaves, torn, plus extra for garnish
salt and pepper

In a food processor or blender, combine half of the artichokes, half of the feta, the garlic and lemon juice with 2 teaspoons of water and blend until smooth.

In a medium bowl, combine the sun-dried tomatoes, pine nuts, basil leaves, the remaining artichokes and the remaining feta cheese. Then add the purée from the step above and mix together well.

Check for seasoning and garnish with chopped sun-dried tomatoes and basil. Store in an airtight container in the fridge and it will stay fresh for 3 days.

sweet potato sesame chipotle dip

Velvety with an edge is how I would describe this sweet but spicy recipe. This means it works as well alongside a hot meal as it does as a dip for cold raw vegetables.

makes about 300g

1 medium-to-large sweet potato
1 tbsp ghee, melted
125–150ml water
2 tsp sesame oil
¼–½ tsp dried chipotle chilli (to taste) (or you can use regular chilli flakes)
pinch of Himalayan or sea salt
juice of 1 lime

Preheat the oven to 200°C/gas 6. Peel and cut the sweet potato into 5cm pieces. Spread it out on a baking sheet lined with baking parchment and drizzle with the melted ghee.

Roast in the oven for 20–25 minutes or until nice and tender. Remove from the oven and set aside to cool.

In a food processor, add the sweet potato and all of the remaining ingredients, starting with 125ml water, and process until you have a thick dip-like texture. Add more water to thin if preferred.

lentil and red onion dip

I'm a fan of lentils with almost anything but here their richness complements the dill perfectly. As well as as a dip, I also serve this as a starter or canapé for guests by spooning it on to cucumber rounds and topping with some extra dill. Plus it's delicious served with poached salmon fillets or grilled aubergine.

makes about 275g

½ medium red onion, with skin, halved
2 garlic cloves, with skin
100g dried Puy lentils, washed and drained
1 tsp cumin seeds
2 tbsp extra virgin olive oil
pinch of pepper
pinch of Himalayan or sea salt
juice of 1 lemon
125ml water
20g bunch fresh dill, leaves roughly chopped

Preheat the oven to 200°C/gas 6. Once hot, place the onion and garlic on a baking sheet in the oven for 25 minutes, checking after 15 minutes and keeping a close eye on it to ensure it does not burn. Remove from the oven and leave to cool, then peel.

Meanwhile, put the lentils into a large saucepan. Cover with plenty of water and bring to the boil, then cover and leave to simmer for 25–30 minutes, until tender. Remove from the heat, drain and set aside.

Place the cooked lentils, onion, garlic and all of the remaining ingredients in a food processor and pulse until you have a blended texture. You may need to stop and scrape the sides a couple of times. Add more water if you prefer a thinner texture.

silly dill dip

I call this 'Silly dill dip' because it is so 'silly easy' to make and yet people are always impressed by it. I certainly was when I first tasted it at a friend's house as we nibbled on crudités and drinks before dinner, and then she told me how healthy it was . . . It is really delicious with a beautiful assortment of chopped raw carrots, celery, cucumber, cauliflower, broccoli, fennel and peppers and is also excellent as an accompaniment to salmon.

makes 500g

20g bunch fresh dill, thick stems chopped
    off (or 10g prepared weight)
5–6 tbsp capers, drained of vinegar
200g small cornichons or gherkins (about
    12–15), drained of vinegar
300g plain Greek yoghurt
juice of 1 lemon
1 tsp Worcestershire sauce

Blend the dill, capers and cornichons or gherkins in a food processor. Once smooth, mix into yoghurt and add the lemon juice and Worcestershire sauce.

roasted beetroot and adzuki bean dip

If looks were everything, this recipe would win every time (see photo on page 211). When you make this, it is a good opportunity to roast a large quantity of beetroot; you can use the extra in the delicious Roasted root, spiced pecan and quinoa salad (see page 188).

makes 700g

3 medium raw beetroot (or pre-boiled if you are in a rush), scrubbed but not peeled

2 tbsp extra virgin olive oil

1 tsp salt

½ tsp pepper

1 medium red onion, roughly chopped

3 garlic cloves, finely chopped

2 tsp balsamic vinegar

1 x 400g can adzuki beans, drained and rinsed

60g plain cashew nuts, soaked in water overnight (or as long as you can), drained

1½ tbsp apple cider vinegar

Preheat the oven to 180°C/gas 4. Place your beetroot in a roasting tin with half the olive oil, the salt and pepper. Roast for 40–45 minutes, until tender. Cool, then peel, chop into small pieces and set aside.

In a large sauté pan, heat the remaining oil over a medium heat and add the onion and garlic. Fry for 10 minutes or until golden. Stir in the balsamic vinegar and turn off the heat. Leave to cool to room temperature then transfer to your food processor with the adzuki beans, caramelised onions, cashews, apple cider vinegar and an extra pinch of salt into. Blend until smooth. Taste and add more salt and pepper if needed.

my little sister's epic guacamole

Whenever we have family gatherings, the guacamole is my sister's territory. No one even tries to make it better than she does. I asked her to spill her secrets for you and I hope you think it's as epic as we do. She tends to taste as she goes, adding a little more lime and salt if she thinks it could use a bit more – it all depends on how juicy your limes are, the strength of your onion, how watery your tomatoes are, etc., so just use your palate to get it to suit your tastes.

makes 675g

½ yellow onion, finely chopped

10g coriander, leaves picked and finely chopped

juice of 2 large limes

5 medium–large avocados (slightly soft to the touch), pitted, peeled and halved

2 medium tomatoes (not too ripe; juicy ones are best), diced

1 jalapeño pepper, finely chopped (optional)

½ tsp ground cumin

½ tsp salt, or to taste

coriander sprig and lime wedge to garnish

Mash the onion, coriander, and the juice of one of the limes to combine the flavours. A traditional molcajete (or large mortar and pestle) is best, but a bowl and sturdy fork can do the trick as well.

Add the avocado and mash lightly with a fork but leave chunky. Stir gently to mix, then add the tomatoes, jalapeño (if using), the juice of the second lime, cumin and salt to taste. Stir to combine, then garnish with a sprig of coriander and a lime wedge.

great green tahini sauce

This sauce is heavenly both in terms of its look and its taste. It's also one of my favourite 'throw it all in the blender' ideas that is great as a dip, a salad dressing or as an accompaniment to meat or fish.

makes 300ml

2 garlic cloves
20g bunch mint, leaves picked
10g bunch flat-leaf parsley, leaves picked
30g watercress leaves (thick stems removed)
1 tsp Himalayan or sea salt
125g tahini
3 tbsp fresh lemon juice
185ml boiling water
1 tsp raw honey (**optional**)

Put the garlic, herbs, watercress, salt, tahini and lemon juice in a blender. Add the boiling water. Let the water and ingredients sit for a minute (this wilts the herbs perfectly), then blend until smooth.

Add honey if you like for extra sweetness, and add more water if you want it to be thinner. Depending on what you are using the sauce for, you may want it thicker or thinner. You can also add more lemon juice or salt to taste if you want.

no-sugar peanut sauce

Shop-bought Asian sauces are generally loaded with ingredients you want to avoid (sugar, salt, preservatives and artificial additives), and peanut dipping sauce is high on the list of culprits. But this recipe saves the day! It's sugar-free yet just as delicious. It's the perfect accompaniment for my Herb and baked tofu summer rolls (see page 191).

makes about 100ml

75g creamy peanut butter (unsweetened)
4 tbsp water
2 tbsp tamari
2 tbsp rice vinegar
1/8 tsp cayenne pepper
juice of 1 lime

Simply pop all your ingredients in the blender and whizz until smooth. Store in the fridge in an airtight container and this will keep well for up to 5 days.

If you're having guests over, make my GREAT GREEN TAHINI SAUCE ahead of time and keep it chilled in the fridge — it will last for 3 days. Shake or stir before serving.

creamy avocado and pepper dressing

If you are as excited as I am about a super-creamy, rich dressing that doesn't contain a drop of dairy, then this is one for you to try. Its decadent and nutritious qualities are great on simple lettuce salads, shredded cabbage slaws or as a dip for raw chopped vegetables. I also often use it as a spread for sandwiches instead of mayonnaise.

makes 275ml

1 large avocado, pitted and peeled
2 tbsp fresh lemon juice
1 tbsp apple cider vinegar
4 tbsp extra virgin olive oil
2 garlic cloves
¼ tsp cayenne pepper
1 tsp raw honey (optional)
salt and pepper

Place all the ingredients in a blender or food processor, along with 125–250ml water, depending on the desired consistency. Blend until creamy.

If you store it in an airtight container in the fridge, it will last for up to 6 days.

tastiest tamari dressing

I admit I am slightly obsessed with this recipe. Bursting with flavours and aromas, it brings any salad to life the instant it is drizzled over the top. I love that something so simple can transform 'just a salad' into a meal you want to eat over and over again. Dressings like this make plant-based living so easy, no matter what stage of the journey you are at.

makes 400ml

125ml extra virgin olive oil
4 tbsp sesame oil
4 tbsp tamari
4 tbsp rice vinegar
4 tbsp apple cider vinegar
2 shallots, halved
3 tbsp white miso paste
5cm ginger, peeled and chopped
juice of ½ lemon
sprinkle of pepper

Add all the ingredients to your blender and blitz together until smooth. Keep refrigerated and it will last well for 5 days.

spicy tahini coconut dressing

This is one of my favourite dressings. It has a wonderfully creamy texture, a fresh lemon zing and a spicy finish, which all blend together perfectly. I love it on shredded carrot and fennel salads, spiralised courgettes or spinach salads with chunks of avocado.

makes 300ml

185ml canned coconut milk
3 tbsp white miso paste
55g almond butter
½ tsp cayenne pepper (or 1 tsp if you really
   like a kick)
2 garlic cloves, finely chopped
125g tahini
3 tbsp fresh lemon juice

Place all the ingredients in a blender or food processor and whizz until completely smooth.

Store in an airtight container in the fridge and it will last for up to 6 days. To use after refrigeration, simply thin to desired consistency with a little water.

lemon tofu mayo

If you are drawn to the taste and texture of traditional mayonnaise, then this is a terrific swap to try. The lemon flavour is fresh and the tofu texture keeps everything light and creamy. This new mayo creation tastes delicious served with steamed artichokes, grilled fish, lamb and roasted vegetables, or it is terrific on sandwiches or used as a dip for raw vegetables.

makes 350ml

300g silken tofu
1 tbsp extra virgin olive oil
juice of 1 lemon
2 tsp lemon zest
¾ tsp Dijon mustard
½ tsp ground turmeric
1 tsp raw honey
¼ tsp salt
¼ tsp ground black pepper
3 tsp white miso paste
2 tsp brown rice vinegar

Purée all the ingredients together in a food processor until smooth. Taste for seasoning and serve. Keep refrigerated and it will last well for up to 3 days.

index

a

açai powder 89
addictive foods 103–4, 120
adzuki beans 87
roasted beetroot and aduzuki
    dip 245
agave nectar (syrup) 106
alcohol consumption 111
almond 46, 78, 200–1, 233
    tamari almonds 217
    zesty lemon coconut
        almonds 217
almond butter 46, 78, 178,
    220–1, 249
almond flour 77, 148
almond milk 46, 78–9, 166–7,
    170–1, 223, 232
    overnight oats 159
    pancakes 162–3
    smoothies 178–9
amaranth 66, 75, 161
amino acids 26, 66, 70, 88, 90,
    92, 97
anti-nutrients 74
apple 166–7, 171, 179
apple crumble smoothie 179
apple cider vinegar 93
apricot and thyme gluten-free
    tart 233
arame 97
artichoke
    marinated artichoke 97
    sun-dried tomato and
        artichoke dip 242
avocado
    creamy avocado and pepper
        dressing 248
    green buzz popsicles 238–9
    my avocado on toast 174–5
    my little sister's epic
        guacamole 245
    smoothies 178–9
    TLAT sandwich 194–5

b

balsamic vinegar 93
banana 161, 178, 236–7
    banana, pecan, and cacao
        nib muffins 223
    peanut butter and banana
        overnight oats 159
baobab powder 89

barley 66, 75
barleygrass powder 90
basil
    basil beauty smoothie 179
    basil mango popsicles 238–9
    basil pesto 240–1
bean(s) 87
    dried 46
    tempeh chilli 187
    see also specific beans
bee pollen 90, 222
beef production 21
beetroot
    beetroot and coconut 'red'
        pancakes 164–5
    feel the beet smoothie 176,
        178
    pasta with summer beets
        and Swiss chard 196–7
    roasted beetroot and adzuki
        dip 245
    roasted root, spiced pecan
        and quinoa salad 188–9
black bean 87, 187, 210–13,
    228–9
    black bean burgers 32, 48,
        71, 208–9
blood pressure, high 20
blood sugar levels 103, 104
blueberry 158–9, 171, 178
    blueberry and coconut
        oatmeal bake 166–7
    blueberry mint vegan ice
        cream 236–7
body weight 20, 103
breadcrumbs 192, 208–9
breakfast 22, 71, 104, 122–33, 144
    sugar swaps 114, 127, 132,
        144
broccoli 210–11
    broccoli 'meatballs' 200–1
brownies (chocolate), two
    ways 58, 228–9
buckwheat 66
    buckwheat tabbouleh 182–3
    chocolate, cranberry and
        buckwheat cookies 226–7
    cooking times 75
    gluten-free buckwheat
        pancakes 162–5
    hazelnut and mushroom
        buckwheat risotto 206–7

raw buckwheat groats 66
toasted buckwheat groats 66
buckwheat flour 77, 223
bulgur wheat 66–7, 75
burgers, black bean 32, 48, 71,
    208–9
burritos 71
butternut squash, roasted root,
    spiced pecan and quinoa
    salad 188–9

c

cacao nibs 23–4
    banana, pecan, and cacao
        nib muffins 223
cacao powder 23–4, 94, 120,
    220–1, 224–5
    chocolate, cranberry and
        buckwheat cookies 226–7
    chocolate brownies 228–9
    chocolatey coconut vegan
        ice cream 236–7
    matcha cacao macaroons
        222
cannellini beans 87, 204
capers 94
carbohydrates,
    simple/complex 103
carbonated drinks 118
carob powder 94, 120
carrot 184–6, 190–1, 193
cashew butter 80
    cashew and raspberry
        overnight oats 158–9
cashew cream 80
cinnamon 232
cashew nut 23–4, 80, 156–7,
    245
    cashew thumbprint cookies
        230–1
cauliflower couscous, Calgary
    180–1
cheese
    kale and tofu enchiladas
        202–3
    vegan lasagne 214–16
    see also specific cheeses
cheesecake, frozen raw
    matcha 23–4
chia seeds 88, 143, 223
    chia seed pudding 129,
        170–1

sunshine sunflower balls
220–1
chicken fingers, healthy 148
chickpea 46, 87, 180–1
  spiced chickpea, brown rice
    and veggie soup 193
  sweet potato, kale and
    chickpea coconut curry 205
  tamari ginger roasted
    chickpeas 219
children's diets 13, 32, 136–53
  breakfasts 104, 132
  condiments 94
  food shopping 48
  getting them involved 40,
    48, 151
  visual appeal 153
chilli, my mom's tempeh 187
chipotle dip, sweet potato
  sesame 242
chlorella 90
chocolate 120
  chocolate, cranberry and
    buckwheat cookies 226–7
  chocolate brownies, two
    ways 228–9
  chocolate-fix smoothie 179
  chocolatey coconut vegan
    ice cream 236–7
cinnamon cashew cream 232
cleaning vegetables 93
coconut 81–4, 222
coconut butter 81
coconut cream 81, 128
coconut (desiccated) 170–1,
  220–1, 233
  blueberry and coconut
    oatmeal bake 166–7
  brown rice coconut porridge
    156–7
  chocolaty coconut vegan ice
    cream 236–7
  coconut spirulina energy
    balls 224–5
  sweet quinoa and coconut
    morning pud 161
coconut flakes 81, 83, 168–9
coconut flour 77
coconut milk 83, 220–1
  beetroot and coconut 'red'
    pancakes 164–5
  blueberry and coconut
    oatmeal bake 166–7
  brown rice coconut porridge
    156–7
  chia seed pudding 170–1

coco-strawberry popsicles
  238–9
courgette `bread' porridge
  160
making your own 84
'milkshakes' 145
overnight oats 158–9
smoothies 178
super scrambles 172–3
sweet potato, kale and
  chickpea coconut curry 205
sweet quinoa and coconut
  morning pud 161
coconut oil 84
coconut sugar 106–7
coconut water 84, 160, 177–9,
  238–9
coconut yoghurt 111, 228
condiments 93–4
cookies
  cashew thumbprint 230–1
  chocolate, cranberry and
    buckwheat 226–7
cooking methods 42
cooking oils 93
cornichons (gherkins) 244
courgette 198–9, 214–16
  courgette 'bread' porridge
    160
  feta, quinoa and pine nut
    stuffed courgettes 204
couscous, Calgary cauliflower
  180–1
cranberry, buckwheat and
  chocolate cookies 226–7
C.R.A.P., cutting the 118
cravings 103, 119
cream
  cashew 80
  cinnamon cashew 232
  hazelnut 206–7
cucumber 179, 182–3
curry 117
  curried wild rice salad 184–5
  sweet potato, kale and
    chickpea coconut curry
    205

dates 159, 161, 171, 179,
  224–5, 231
diabetes, type 2 20, 103
diets, giving up on 11, 13
dill dip, silly 244
dips 242–5
dressings 248–9

drinks
  carbonated 118
  fruit juice 108, 145
  sugar swaps 117
  water intake 145
dulse 94

eating out 22–3, 148
edamame 87, 92
egg 130, 198–9
  curried devilled egg 47
  hard-boiled eggs 46, 47, 129
  polenta and eggs 70
  scrambled eggs 48, 129
  super scrambles 172–3
enchiladas, kale and tofu
  202–3
endorphins 118
endosperm 64
energy roller coaster 103–4,
  114

fats 23
feta 192, 212–13, 242
  feta, quinoa and pine nut
    stuffed courgettes 204
figgy pudding popsicles 238–9
fish fingers, healthy 148
flaxseed 88, 222
flours 77
food labels 102, 104, 113
food shopping 48, 113
freekeh 67, 75
freezers 36, 39, 50–8
fridges 36, 39, 46
fructose 106–8
fruit 108–11
  dried 118
  see also specific fruits
fruit juice 108, 145
fruit yoghurts 111
fussy eaters 146

GI *see* glycaemic index
ginger tamari roasted
  chickpeas 219
glucose 103
gluten, elimination 11, 64
gluten-free foods 64, 66–73
  gluten-free apricot and
    thyme tart 233
  gluten-free buckwheat
    pancakes 162–5

glycaemic index (GI) 104, 106–7
goat's cheese 180–1, 238–9
goji berries 97
grains 23, 64–75
granola, low-sugar 129, 168–9
grapefruit 179
grapes, frozen 58
green buzz popsicles 238–9
green goodness smoothie 179
guacamole 71, 212–13
    my little sister's epic guacamole 245

h
halloumi and lentil Mediterranean salad 186
hazelnut 224–5
    hazelnut cream 206–7
    hazelnut and mushroom buckwheat risotto 206–7
heart disease 20, 103
hemp seed 88
    hemp seed pesto 240–1
herbs
    freezing 52
    herb and baked tofu summer rolls 190–1

i
ice cream, vegan 236–7

k
kale
    freezing 52
    kale and tofu enchiladas 202–3
    smoothies 178–9
    sweet potato, kale and chickpea coconut curry 205
kedgeree 47
khorasan wheat (kamut) 67, 75
kombu 97

l
lasagne, vegan 58, 214–16
leek 187, 206–7
    spinach and leek 'green' pancakes 164–5
leftovers 25, 130
legumes 87
lemon 178–9
    lemon tofu mayo 249
    lemon vinaigrette 188–9
zesty lemon coconut almonds 217
lentil 87
    halloumi and lentil Mediterranean salad 186
    how to cook 44
    lentil and red onion dip 244
lettuce, TLAT sandwich 194–5
lucuma 90
lunch boxes, plant-based 25, 145

m
maca powder 90, 163, 278
    maca smoothie 176, 178
macadamia 23–4
macaroons, matcha cacao 222
mango basil popsicles 238–9
maple syrup 107
marketing 113
matcha 90, 238
    frozen raw matcha cheesecake 23–4
    matcha cacao macaroon 222
mayo, lemon tofu 249
milks, dairy
milks, plant-based 140
    see also specific milks
'milkshakes' 145
millet 67, 75, 161
mint 180–1, 188–9
    blueberry mint vegan ice cream 236–7
miso paste 93
    miso brown rice 68
moringa powder 90–2
muffins, banana, pecan, and cacao nib 58, 223
mushroom 130
    hazelnut and mushroom buckwheat risotto 206–7
    pesto Portobello mushrooms 192
mustard 93

n
nori 97
nut butters 78, 80
    see also specific nuts
nuts 46, 78–80
    low-sugar granola 168–9
    see also specific nuts

o
oats 179, 220–1, 230–1
    blueberry and coconut oatmeal bake 166–7
    courgette 'bread' porridge 160
    low-sugar granola 168–9
    overnight oats 46, 158–9
    rolled oats 73, 75
    steel-cut oats 73
obesity 20, 103
olive oil 93
olives 97, 184–5, 212–13
onion 187, 192, 204
    lentil and red onion dip 244
orange 176, 178
organisation 34–58, 128–9, 140
organic produce 30–1, 111
overweight 103

p
palm hearts 97
pancakes 32, 114
    gluten-free buckwheat 162–5
pantry clear outs 118, 140
pantry staples 36, 39, 60–97
pasta 117
    pasta sauces 32, 58
    pasta with summer beets and Swiss chard 196–7
    tomato pasta sauce 130
    vegan lasagne 214–16
peanut 80
    no-sugar peanut sauce 247
peanut butter 80
    peanut butter and banana overnight oats 159
pea(s) 182–3, 198–9
pecan 184–5
    banana, pecan, and cacao nib muffins 223
    roasted root, spiced pecan and quinoa salad 188–9
    spiced pecans 218
pepper 184–6, 198–9, 210–11
    creamy avocado and pepper dressing 248
pesto 130
    pesto Portobello mushrooms 192
    pesto, three ways 240–1
physical exercise 11, 118
phytic acid 74
pine nut, feta and quinoa stuffed courgettes 204

pineapple, smoothies 178–9
pink power overnight oats
    158–9
planning ahead 34–58, 128–9,
    140
plant-based real food 10–11,
    13
plate, ideal 23
plums, autumn spiced plums
    and cinnamon cashew
    cream 232
polenta 70, 75, 130, 148
pomegranate 46, 171, 180–1
popcorn 153
popsicles 153
    four ways 238–9
porridge 129
    brown rice coconut porridge
        156–7
    courgette 'bread' porridge
        160
power supplements 89–92
prep days 42–7, 58
processed food, giving up on
    10–11, 16, 18, 64, 118
processed/refined food, giving
    up on 10, 11, 16, 18, 64, 118
protein 23, 26–7
protein powders, plant-based
    92
pseudo-grains 64–5
pumpkin seeds 88
purées 32, 143
purple power chia seed
    pudding 171

quinoa 58, 70–1
    cooking times 75
    feta, quinoa and pine nut
        stuffed courgettes 204
    roasted root, spiced pecan
        and quinoa salad 188–9
    spiced quinoa 68
    sweet quinoa and coconut
        morning pud 161
    toasted quinoa 70
quinoa flakes 70
quinoa flour 77

raisin(s) 160, 184–5
raspberry
    and coconut brownies by
        Made by Margie 228–9
    cashew and raspberry

overnight oats 158–9
real food 8, 10–11, 13, 16
refined food, giving up on
    10–11, 16, 18, 64, 118
rewards 119, 140
rice (black) 66
rice (brown) 58, 66
    brown rice bowls of
        goodness 210–11
    brown rice coconut porridge
        156–7
    brown rice coconut pudding
        130
    cooking times 75
    miso brown rice 68
    rainbow fried rice 198–9
    spiced chickpea, brown rice
        and veggie soup 193
rice (wild) 58, 73
    cooking times 75
    curried wild rice salad 184–5
rice paper 190–1
risotto, hazelnut and
    mushroom buckwheat 206–7
rye 75

salads 22–3, 46, 48, 114
    curried wild rice 184–5
    halloumi and lentil
        Mediterranean 186
    Middle Eastern 44
    quinoa for 71
        roasted root, spiced pecan
            and quinoa 188–9
sandwiches 114
    home-made 25
    TLAT (tempeh, lettuce,
        avocado and tomato) 194–5
seasonal produce 28–9
seaweed, dried 94–7
seeds 88–9, 168–9, 220–1
sesame chipotle sweet potato
    dip 242
sesame oil 93
sesame seeds 88–9
shopping lists 39–40
smoothies 48, 108, 129, 143,
    176–9
snacks 117, 119, 152
soup 114, 136
    spiced chickpea, brown rice
        and veggie 193
    vegetable 25, 71
soya bean 87, 92
spinach 48, 214–16

smoothies 176, 178–9
spinach and leek 'green'
    pancakes 164–5
spinach pesto 240–1
spirulina 92, 224
steaming 42
stevia 107
strawberry 178
    coco-strawberry popsicles
        238–9
sucrose 100
sugar 98–120
    and alcohol 111
    alternatives 106–7
    average consumption levels
        105
    elimination 11, 13, 112–19
    and fruit 108–11
    health implications 103
    hidden 104–5, 127, 144
sunflower seeds 89
    sunshine sunflower balls
        220–1
superfood smoothie 176, 178
sweet potato
    baked sweet potato boats
        with tasty toppings 212–13
    sweet potato, kale and
        chickpea coconut curry
        205
    sweet potato sesame
        chipotle dip 242
sweetcorn 212–13
sweeteners 100, 102, 128
Swiss chard, summer beets
    and pasta 196–7

tabbouleh, buckwheat 182–3
tahini
    great green tahini sauce 247
    spicy tahini coconut
        dressings 249
tamari 94
    tamari almonds 217
    tamari baked tofu 210–11
    tamari ginger roasted
        chickpeas 219
    tastiest tamari dressing 248
tart, gluten-free apricot and
    thyme 233
teff 73, 75
tempeh
    my mom's tempeh chilli 187
    sweet potato, kale and
        chickpea coconut curry 205

TLAT (tempeh, lettuce, avocado and tomato) sandwich 194–5
toast, my avocado on 174–5
tofu 210–11, 214–16
  herb and baked tofu summer rolls 190–1
  kale and tofu enchiladas 202–3
  lemon tofu mayo 249
  tamari baked tofu 210–11
  tofu sauce 214–16
tomato 182–3, 187, 193, 214–16, 245
  sun-dried 97, 242
  sun-dried tomato and artichoke dip 242

tomato pasta sauce 130
tomato sauce 202–3
tortillas 202–3
tropical green smoothie 178

V
vegan diet 19
  vegan ice cream 236–7
  vegan lasagne 58, 214–16
vegetables, cleaning 93
vegetarian diet 19
vinaigrette, lemon 188–9

W
wakame 94
walnut 80
  chocolate and walnut

brownies by Roots & Bulbs 228–9
water intake 145
wheat, elimination 11, 64
wheat-free foods 64
wheatgrass 92
whole grains 64
wine 111
wraps 25

X
xylitol 107

Y
yeast, nutritional 97
yoghurt 127, 238–9, 244
  fruit yoghurts 111

First published in Great Britain
in 2016 by Yellow Kite
An imprint of Hodder & Stoughton
An Hachette UK company

1

Text copyright © Calgary Avansino 2016
Photography copyright © Kristin Perers 2016

A CIP catalogue record for this title is available from the British Library

Hardback ISBN 9781473619210
eBook ISBN 9781473619234

www.hodder.co.uk
www.calgaryavansino.com

Publisher: Liz Gough
Design and art direction: Nikki Dupin
Project editor: Imogen Fortes
Photography: Kristin Perers
Food styling: Aya Nishimura
Prop styling: Linda Berlin
Hair: Diana Moar
Make up: Emma O'Byrne and Faye Quinton
Content coordinator: Grace Carter

Printed and bound in Germany by Mohn Media GmbH, Gütersloh

Hodder & Stoughton policy is to use papers that are natural, renewable and recyclable products and made from wood grown in sustainable forests. The logging and manufacturing processes are expected to conform to the environ¬mental regulations of the country of origin.

The advice herein is not intended to replace the services of trained health professionals, or be a substitute for medical advice. Consult with your health care professional with regard to your health, and in particular regarding matters that may require diagnosis or medical attention.

Hodder & Stoughton Ltd
Carmelite House
50 Victoria Embankment
London EC4Y 0DZ

acknowledgements

It's really not fair that only my name goes on the cover of this book! Without the help, support, guidance and patience of so many amazing talents, it would not be the gorgeous finished product it is today. A gigantic thank you and sincere gratitude to:

- **Skip**, **Kristen**, **Marisa** and **Pat**, my beloved family who tried recipes, read chapters, listened to all my fears and, most importantly, pushed me forward… One step at a time.
- **Don**, who I'd marry all over again, which pretty much says it all.
- **Kristin Perers** – I feel blessed and grateful to have shared this process with you. It could have been difficult and stressful but every day shooting with you was a fun, creative, inspiring experience… And I'm not just saying that either!
- **Liz Gough**, for believing there was a book in me long before I did. You have always listened, always given the best advice and have truly defined what an excellent publisher should be.
- **Imogen Fortes**, for editing my every word with expert knowledge and genuine care. You got me, you got my food, and I will be forever grateful we were paired.
- **Grace Carter**, for being the most detail-oriented person I've ever met. Without you I wouldn't be writing this page.
- **Linda Berlin**, for creating beauty in every setting and at every angle.
- **Aya Nishimura**, for your mastery in the kitchen, making every recipe come to life.
- **Nikki Dupin**, for loving my wallpaper and for bringing my character to every page of the book.
- **Diana Moar**, for your friendship, your talented hands, your epic braids and your brilliant ideas.

- **Emma O'Byrne**, **Faye Quinton** and **Arabella Preston**, for making me camera-ready, even when I'd had very little sleep and hormonal skin – you are geniuses.
- **Rachel Wood**, for helping me feel reassured that every recipe is 100 per cent book ready.
- **Margie Broadhead** ('Made by Margie') and **Sarah Cadji** (Roots & Bulbs), for sharing your mouthwatering recipes.
- **Sarah Christie**, for making us do it again… You know your stuff.
- **Caitriona Horne**, for having endless good ideas and acting on them.
- **Wilma**, for making it possible for me to leave my babies with peace of mind and for sharing this food journey with me.
- **Veronique Norton**, for spreading the *Keep It Real* word better than anyone.
- **Charlotte Sinclair**, for your keen reads, your honest feedback, your friendship and your time.
- **Clara Pierucci** and **Eve Kalinik**, for your decadent inspiration.
- **Josh Wood**, for the locks, the laughs and the love.
- **Alexandra Shulman**, for believing in me since I was 24; I have grown up with you by my side.
- **Tom** and **Molly**, for generous and genius guidance.
- **Anthropologie**, for your bright colours and generosity.
- **FlowerBX**, for bringing the best, fresh flowers to London.
- **Bodas**, for making bedtime better.